Nuffield Primary Science
SCIENCE PROCESSES AND CONCEPT EXPLORATION

Rocks, soil and weather

Ages
7-12

TEACHERS' GUIDE

PUBLISHED FOR THE NUFFIELD–CHELSEA CURRICULUM TRUST BY COLLINS EDUCATIONAL

Trial schools

The SPACE Project and the Trust are grateful to the governors, staff, and pupils of all the trial schools. It will be obvious to readers of these guides how much we are indebted to them for their help, and especially for the children's drawn and written records of their hard work and their growing understanding of science.

All Saints Primary School, Barnet, Hertfordshire
Ansdell County Primary School, Lytham St Anne's, Lancashire
Bishop Endowed Church of England Junior School, Blackpool
Brindle Gregson Lane Primary School, Lancashire
Brookside Junior and Infants School, Knowsley
Chalgrove JMI School, Finchley, London N3
Christ the King Roman Catholic Primary School, Blackpool
English Martyrs Roman Catholic Primary School, Knowsley
Fairlie County Primary School, Skelmersdale, Lancashire
Fairway JMI School, Mill Hill, London NW7
Foulds Primary School, Barnet, Hertfordshire
Frenchwood County Primary School, Preston
Grange Park Primary School, London N21
Hallesville Primary School, Newham, London E6
Heathmore Primary School, Roehampton, London SW15
Honeywell Junior School, London SW11
Huyton Church of England Junior School, Knowsley
Longton Junior School, Preston
Mawdesley Church of England Primary School, Lancashire
Moor Park Infants School, Blackpool
Mosscroft County Primary School, Knowsley
Nightingale Primary School, London E18
Oakhill Primary School, Woodford Green, Essex
Park Brow County Primary School, Knowsley
Park View Junior School, Knowsley
Purford Green Junior School, Harlow, Essex
Ronald Ross Primary School, London SW19
Rosh Pinah School, Edgeware, Middlesex
Sacred Heart Junior School, Battersea, London SW11
St Aloysius Roman Catholic Infants School, Knowlsey
St Andrew's Roman Catholic Primary School, Knowsley
St Bernadette's Roman Catholic Primary School, Blackpool
St James's Church of England Junior School, Forest Gate, London E7
St John Fisher Roman Catholic Primary School, Knowsley
St John Vianney Roman Catholic Primary School, Blackpool
St Mary and St Benedict Roman Catholic Primary School, Bamber Bridge, Preston
St Peter and St Paul Roman Catholic Primary School, Knowsley
St Theresa's Roman Catholic Primary School, Blackpool
St Theresa's Roman Catholic Primary School, Finchley, London N3
Scarisbrick County Primary School, Lancashire
Selwyn Junior School, London E4
Snaresbrook Primary School, Wanstead, London E18
South Grove Primary School, Walthamstow, London E17
Southmead Infants School, London SW19
Staining Church of England Primary School, Blackpool
Walton-le-Dale County Primary School, Preston
West Vale County Primary School, Kirkby
Woodridge Primary School, North Finchley, London N12

NUFFIELD PRIMARY SCIENCE
Science Processes and Concept Exploration

Directors
Paul Black
Wynne Harlen

Deputy Director
Terry Russell

Project members
Robert Austin
Derek Bell
Adrian Hughes
Ken Longden
John Meadows
Linda McGuigan
Jonathan Osborne
Pamela Wadsworth
Dorothy Watt

First published 1993 by Collins Educational
An imprint of HarperCollins*Publishers*
77-85 Fulham Palace Road
London W6 8JB

Second edition published 1995
Reprinted 1996

Copyright © Nuffield-Chelsea Curriculum Trust 1993, 1995

ISBN 0 00 310260 2

Printed and bound in Hong Kong

Design by Carla Turchini, Chi Leung
Illustrations by Hemesh Alles, John Booth, Gay Galsworthy, Maureen Hallahan, Helen Herbert, Sally Neave, Rhian Nest-James, Karen Tushingham
Cover artwork by Karen Tushingham

Photograph acknowledgements
Page 28: Hutchison Library
Page 60 (left): Rex Features
Page 60 (right): Catherine Blackie

Commissioned photography by Oliver Hatch

The Trust and the Publishers would like to thank the governors, staff and pupils of Hillbrook Primary School, Tooting, for their kind co-operation with many of the photographs in this book.

Safety adviser
Peter Borrows

Other contributors
Elizabeth Harris
Carol Joyes
Anne de Normanville
Ralph Hancock

Contents

Chapter 1

Introduction   *page 5*

1.1 The SPACE approach to teaching and
learning science   5
1.2 Useful strategies   6
1.3 Equal opportunities   7
1.4 Rocks, soil and weather and the curriculum   8
1.5 Experimental and Investigative Science   10

Chapter 2

Planning   *page 12*

2.1 Introduction: planning with children's
ideas in mind   12
2.2 Cross-curricular topics   12
2.3 Topic plan examples   14
2.4 Use of information technology   14
2.5 Pupils' books   14
2.6 Planning your science programme in school   22
2.7 Resources   25
2.8 Warnings   25

Chapter 3

Exploring rocks, soil and weather   *page 27*

Theme organizer   27
3.1 Rocks and soils   28
A look at rocks and soils   29
Finding out children's ideas: starter activities   30
Children's ideas   35
Helping children to develop their ideas   44
3.2 Weather   60
A look at weather   61
Finding out children's ideas: starter activities   62
Children's ideas   64
Helping children to develop their ideas   68

Chapter 4

Assessment   *page 74*

Chapter 5

Background science   *page 81*

Index   *page 96*

Explanation of symbols in the margins

 Warning

 Good opportunities to develop and assess work related to Experimental and Investigative Science

 Notes which may be useful to the teacher

 Vocabulary work

 Opportunities for children to use information technology

 Equipment needed

 Reference to the pupils' books

CHAPTER 1

Introduction

1.1 The SPACE approach to teaching and learning science

A primary class where the SPACE approach to science is being used may not at first seem different from any other class engaged in science activities; in either, children will be mentally and physically involved in exploring objects and events in the world around them. However, a closer look will reveal that both the children's activities and the teacher's role differ from those found in other approaches. The children are not following instructions given by others; they are not solving a problem set them by someone else. They are deeply involved in work which is based on their own ideas, and they have taken part in deciding how to do it.

The teacher has, of course, prepared carefully to reach the point where children try out their ideas. She or he will have started on the topic by giving children opportunities to explore from their own experience situations which embody important scientific ideas. The teacher will have ensured that the children have expressed their ideas about what they are exploring, using one or more of a range of approaches – from whole class discussion to talking with individual children, or asking children to write or draw – and will have explored the children's reasons for having those ideas.

With this information the teacher will have decided how to help the children to develop or revise their ideas. That may involve getting the children to use the ideas to make a prediction, then testing it by seeing if it works in practice; or the children may gather further evidence to discuss and think about. In particular, the teacher will note how 'scientific' children have been in their gathering and use of evidence; and should, by careful questioning, encourage greater rigour in the use of scientific process skills.

It is essential that the children change their ideas only as a result of what they find themselves, not by merely accepting ideas which they are told are better.

By carefully exploring children's ideas, taking them seriously and choosing appropriate ways of helping the children to test them, the teacher can move children towards ideas which apply more widely and fit the evidence better – those which are, in short, more scientific.

You will find more information about the SPACE approach in the Nuffield Primary Science *Science Co-ordinators' handbook*.

1.2 Useful strategies

Finding out children's ideas

This guide points out many opportunities for finding out children's ideas. One way is simply by talking, but there are many others. We have found the following strategies effective. How you use them may depend on the area of science you are dealing with. In Chapter 3 you will find examples of these strategies. More information about them is given in the *Science Co-ordinators' handbook*.

Talking and open questioning

Whole class discussions can be useful for sharing ideas, but they do not always give all children a chance to speak. It is often helpful if children are allowed to think of their own ideas first, perhaps working them out in drawings, and are then encouraged to share these with others – perhaps with just one other child, or with a larger group.

Annotated drawings

Asking children to draw their ideas can give a particularly clear insight into what they think. It also gives you a chance to discuss the children's ideas with them. Words conveying these ideas can then be added to the drawing, either by you or by the child. Such work can be kept as a permanent record.

Sorting and classifying

This can be a useful way of helping children to clarify their ideas and to record their thinking. They could sort a collection of objects or pictures into groups.

Writing down ideas

Children may instead write down their responses to questions you pose. Writing gives children the opportunity to express their own views, which can then be shared with others or investigated further.

Log books and diaries

These can be used to record changes over a longer investigation. They need not necessarily be kept by individual children, but could be kept by a whole group or class. Children can jot down their ideas, as words or drawings, when they notice changes, recording their reasons for what they observe.

Helping children to develop their ideas

Letting children test their own ideas

This will involve children in using some or all of the process skills of science:

- observing
- measuring
- hypothesizing
- predicting
- planning and carrying out fair tests
- interpreting results and findings
- communicating

It is an important strategy which can, and should, be used often. The *use* of process skills *develops* them – for example, through greater attention to detail in observing, more careful control of variables in fair tests, and taking all the evidence into account in interpreting the results.

Encouraging generalization from one context to another

Does an explanation proposed for a particular event fit one which is not exactly the same, but which involves the same scientific concept? You or the children might suggest other contexts that might be tried. This might be done by discussing the evidence for and against the explanation, or by gathering more evidence and testing the idea in the other context, depending on children's familiarity with the events being examined.

Discussing the words children use to describe their ideas

Children can be asked to be quite specific about the meaning of words they use, whether scientific or not. They can be prompted to think of alternative words which have almost the same meaning. They can discuss, where appropriate, words which have special meaning in a scientific context, and so be helped to realize the difference between the 'everyday' use of some words and the scientific one.

Extending the range of evidence

Some of the children's ideas may be consistent with the evidence at present available to them, but could be challenged by extending the range of evidence. This applies particularly to things which are not easily observed, such as slow changes; or those which are normally hidden, such as the insides of objects. Attempts to make these imperceptible things perceptible, often by using secondary sources, help children to consider a wider range of evidence.

Getting children to communicate their ideas

Expressing ideas in any way – through writing, drawing, modelling or, particularly, through discussion – involves thinking them through, and often rethinking and revising them. Discussion has a further advantage in that it is two-way and children can set others' ideas against their own. Just realizing that there are different ideas helps them to reconsider their own.

1.3 Equal opportunities

The SPACE approach to teaching and learning science gives opportunities for every child to build on and develop his or her experiences, skills and ideas. It can therefore be used to benefit pupils of all kinds and at any stage of development. This is fully discussed in the *Science Co-ordinators' handbook*.

1.4 Rocks, soil and weather and the curriculum

This teachers' guide is divided into two themes; in each one there is a section on finding out children's ideas, examples of ideas children have, and a section on helping children to develop their ideas.

Nuffield Primary Science Themes

Rocks and soils

This theme explores the nature and formation of different types of rocks and soils. The formation of landscape features and the structure of the Earth are introduced. Children's ideas about what is underground vary considerably, but few indicate any recognition of the scale and distances involved. Soil is associated with the material that things grow in, but few children suggest that there is a range of soil types or indicate how the soil got there. Rocks tend to be seen as very large stones; few children seem to be aware of layers of rock lying underground. Ideas about the formation of landscape features are often limited to specific experiences. The activities provide opportunities for children to observe, classify and test rocks and soils of different types in order to examine their properties. Investigations into the factors which affect rocks and soils are suggested to provide help in developing ideas about their formation. Suggestions for visits are included.

Weather

This theme examines changes in the weather and the seasonal patterns that can be identified. The effects of different weather conditions on the environment are introduced. Most children recognize changes in the weather and can often relate these to different times of the day or year. Often the ideas expressed are simple descriptions and many variations are not expressed. The use of satellites figures largely in making weather forecasts, but few children show an awareness of the need to measure various factors in order to make the predictions. The activities include measuring and recording various weather features, and the use of data from secondary sources to investigate the types of weather that actually occur in particular places. Ways of examining the effects of different elements of the weather are suggested. Children also consider the water cycle.

National Curriculum Programmes of Study	Environmental Studies 5-14 (Scotland): Science

Materials and their Properties

1 Grouping and classifying materials
a to compare everyday materials on the basis of their properties, including hardness, strength, flexibility and magnetic behaviour, and to relate these properties to everyday uses of the materials;
d to describe and group rocks and soils on the basis of characteristics, including appearance, texture and permeability.

3 Separating mixtures of materials
a that solid particles of different sizes can be separated by sieving.

Understanding Earth and Space (Stages P4 to P6)

Materials from Earth
• further properties of common materials
Leading on to (Stages P7 to S2)
• materials as elements, compounds.

Materials and their Properties

2 Changing materials
e about the water cycle and the part played by evaporation and condensation.

Weather appears in the Geography National Curriculum at Key Stage 2, not Science. Pupils should be taught about seasonal weather patterns.

Understanding Earth and Space (Stages P4 to P6)

On planet Earth
• the Earth's atmosphere and some effects of having air around the planet;
• the water cycle, introducing water as a gas, melting, freezing, evaporation, condensation;
• patterns of weather observed locally.

1.5 Experimental and Investigative Science

Two important aspects of children's learning in science are:

◆ learning how to investigate the world around them;
◆ learning to make sense of the world around them using scientific ideas.

These are reflected in the National Curriculum. 'Experimental and Investigative Science' covers the first aspect. The second aspect is covered by the rest of the Programme of Study. Although these two aspects of science learning are separated in the National Curriculum they cannot be separated in practice and it is not useful to try to do so. Through investigation children explore their ideas and/or test out the ideas which arise from discussion. As a result, ideas may be advanced, but this will depend on the children's investigation skills. Thus it is important to develop these skills in the context of activities which extend ideas. So there is no separate Nuffield Primary Science teachers' guide on scientific investigations, because opportunities to make these occur throughout all the guides and they form an essential part of the SPACE approach.

Thus in this guide you will find investigations which provide opportunities to develop and assess the skills and understanding set out in Experimental and Investigative Science. These are marked in the text by the symbol shown here. In this teachers' guide, the investigations which cover the most skills are 'Soil and plant growth' (page 53) and 'A weather station' (page 68).

It is important that teachers give active guidance to pupils during investigations to help them work out how to improve the way in which they plan and carry out their investigations.

Experimental and Investigative Science is about the ways scientific evidence can be obtained, about the ways observations and measurements are made, and about the way in which the evidence is analysed. It therefore sets out three main ways in which pupils can develop their ability to do experimental and investigative science, as follows:-

1 'Planning experimental work'. Here, children should be helped to make progress from asking general and vague questions, to suggesting ideas which could be tested. Teachers' discussion with pupils should aim to help them to make predictions, using their existing understanding, on the basis of which they can decide what evidence should be collected. This should lead them to think about what apparatus and equipment they should use.

When children describe plans for their work, they should be helped to think about what features they are going to change, what effects of these changes they are going to observe or measure, and what features they must keep the same. In this way they can come to understand what is meant by 'a fair test'.

2 'Obtaining evidence'. Children should make observations in the light of their ideas about what they are looking for and why. When they describe their observations, teachers may have to help them to improve, for example by reminding them of their original aims and plan for the work. Such help should also encourage progress from qualitative comparisons and judgements to appreciating the value of making quantitative measurements (for example 'cold water' is qualitative, 'water at 12°C' is quantitative). This should lead to the development of skills with a variety of instruments and to increasing care and accuracy in measurement, involving, for example, repeating measurements to check.

3 'Considering evidence'. Here, children should first learn to record their evidence in systematic and clear ways, starting with simple drawings and then learning to use tables, bar charts and line graphs to display the patterns in numerical data. Then they should be asked to think about and discuss their results, considering what might be learnt from any trends or patterns. As ideas develop, they should be careful in checking their evidence against the original idea underlying the investigation and should become increasingly critical in discussing alternative explanations which might fit their evidence. In such discussions, they should be helped to relate their arguments to their developing scientific understanding. They should also be guided to see possibilities for conducting their investigation more carefully, or in quite different ways.

Whilst these three may seem to form a natural sequence of stages, children's work might not follow this particular sequence. For example, some might start with evidence from their observations and proceed on this basis to propose a hypothesis and a plan to test it. For others, the results of one task may be the starting point for a new inquiry involving new measurements. Useful learning about how to investigate might arise when only one or two of the above aspects of an investigation are involved, or when the teacher tells children about some aspects so that they can concentrate on others. However, there should be some occasions for all pupils when they carry out the whole process of investigation by themselves.

The assessment examples given in chapter 4 are analysed in relation to the level descriptions, which describe children's progress in relation to these three aspects: *planning experimental work, obtaining evidence* and *considering evidence*. Thus, these three provide a framework both for guiding children and for assessing their progress in experimental and investigative work.

CHAPTER 2

Planning

2.1 Introduction: planning with children's ideas in mind

The key scientific ideas presented in this guide can be explored in various contexts, and many of the suggested activities can be incorporated into cross-curricular topic work. This chapter uses a worked example as an aid to planning a topic. Further information on planning is given in the *Science Co-ordinators' handbook.*

A teacher using the SPACE approach should take into account:

◆ the need to find out children's own ideas, not only at the beginning of the work but also at intervals during it;
◆ the importance of planning the investigations with the children, using their ideas as the starting point;
◆ the concepts that are being explored;
◆ the direction in which the children's ideas are developing.

2.2 Cross-curricular topics

Activities which explore the ideas covered in this teachers' guide to Rocks, soil and weather may be approached via a number of topics in addition to the one set out as an example in the planning sheets (pages 15-16). It is assumed that teachers will adapt the topic to whatever local resources are of interest and readily to hand. Some possibilities are given below.

Farms and farming

What is a farm, how do farms vary, and how have they developed historically? Medieval strip cultivation; small-holdings and crofts; mixed farms and agri-business.
How do farms affect the way the landscape looks; how would the land look if it were not farmed?
Common land. The history of hedgerows, how they were planted and used; other forms of enclosure.
Farming in other countries – matching crops to the climate.
The interaction of animals and plants, and the use of pesticides.
Animals which are natural pest controllers.
Land use and crops – roots, cereals, dairy, sheep, etc.
Matching crops to the soil type and amount of soil cover. Preparation of the land.
Work at different times of the year.
What treatments are given to the soil? Ploughing. Fertilizers, new and old. Returning nutrients to the soil.

Effects of weather on farming – droughts and floods.
Frozen soil – advantages and disadvantages.
How crops and livestock have changed; animal husbandry – selective breeding.
Plants for purposes: resistance to disease and heavy cropping. The EEC apple – is it a Good Thing?

Some links with other Nuffield Primary Science teachers' guides and pupils' books include:

Living processes – plant growth;
Living things in their environment – changes to the landscape as a result of farming, effects of fertilizers, soil as a habitat;
The variety of life – decay of once-living things;
The Earth in Space – the seasons;
Materials – comparing different types of rock.

Water

Different forms of water supply: nowadays, in different countries, and in the past.
Technology: getting drinking water from salty water.
What happens to water when it boils? What happens when it freezes?
Effects of water on growth of plants.
Effect of water on different materials: weathering, erosion, solubility.
Water and soil: drainage.
Water in the air, measuring moisture, water and rain.
Clouds.
Too much water, too little water.
Rain forests and deserts.
Waterborne diseases.

Some links with other Nuffield Primary Science teachers' guides and pupils' books include:

Materials and *Using energy* – states of water and changes in state;
Living things in their environment – water supply and waste water;
The variety of life – water as requirement for life;
Living processes – water in the human body.

Air

Going up in the air: balloons, aircraft, birds.
Climbing a high mountain: changing experiences of the air, running at altitude.
Measuring air pressure.
Air quality: smoke, fumes, smog. Ozone – at ground level and above.
Breathing apparatus: under the sea, fighting fires.
Moving air: effects of the wind.
Air in the soil.
Working underground: air in mines.
Gas from buried rubbish.
Air in water – fish.

Some links with other Nuffield Primary Science teachers' guides and pupils' books include:

Forces and movement – falling through the air;

Living processes – breathing, smoking and health;
Living things in their environment – ozone, air pollution, the
greenhouse effect;
The Earth in Space – beyond the air!

2.3 Topic plan examples

The plans on pages 15 and 16 illustrate how the science related to
Rocks, soil and weather may be embedded in a cross-curricular topic.
The topic presented is 'Water' and opportunities for exploring
mathematics, language, history, geography, design technology and art
have been indicated on the first plan. On the second plan the science
work has been amplified to illustrate possible areas of exploration based
within the overall topic. It is important to remember these are only
examples and are not intended to be exhaustive.

2.4 Use of information technology

 Specific examples of opportunities to use information
technology are indicated by this symbol in the margin and
referred to in the text. The examples include:

◆ word processing to produce reports of investigations or to give a
  weather report
◆ simple databases to record and analyse data collected about soil,
  rocks and the weather
◆ using a key to identify rocks and soil
◆ using a sensor coupled with a computer to detect and measure
  temperature.

2.5 Pupils' books

The pupils' books accompanying this guide are called *Rocks, Soil and
Weather* for the lower juniors and *More About Rocks, Soil and Weather*
for the upper juniors. The pupils' books are intended to be used spread
by spread. The spreads are not sequential, and they are covered in
these notes in thematic order.

Features of the pupils' books include:
◆ Stimulus spreads, often visual, designed to raise
  questions, arouse curiosity, and to promote discussion.

◆ Information spreads, which give secondary source material
  in a clear and attractive way.

◆ Activity ideas, to form the basis of investigations to be
  carried out by the children.

◆ Cross-curricular spreads and stories which can act as a
  basis for creative writing, or spreads with a historical
  or creative focus.

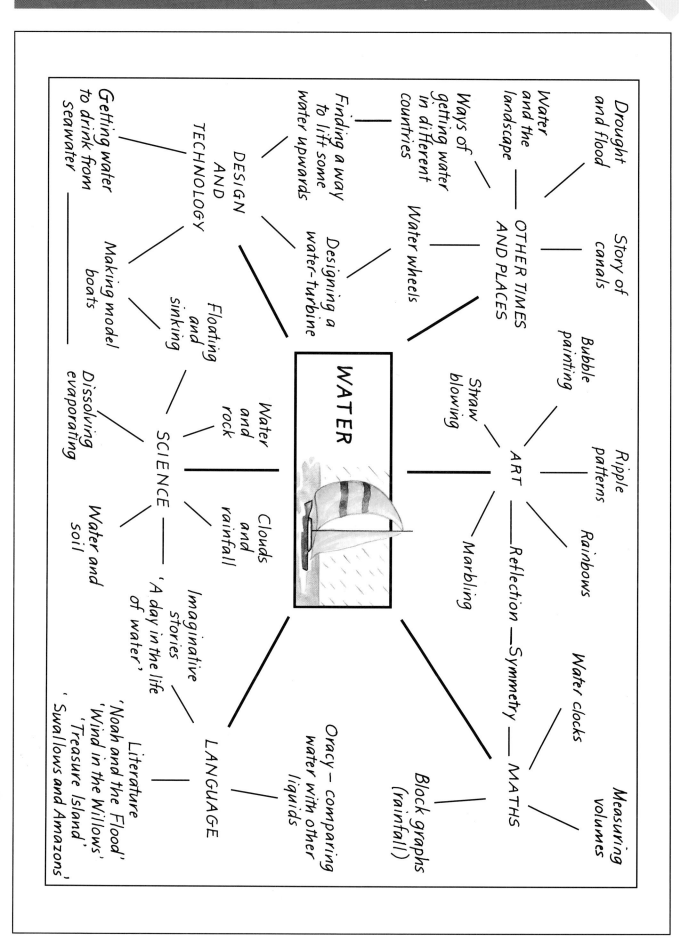

WATER

OTHER TIMES AND PLACES
- Drought and flood
- Water and the landscape
- Story of canals
- Ways of getting water in different countries
- Water wheels

DESIGN AND TECHNOLOGY
- Finding a way to lift some water upwards
- Designing a water-turbine
- Getting water to drink from seawater
- Making model boats
- Floating and sinking

SCIENCE
- Dissolving evaporating
- Water and soil
- Water and rock
- Clouds and rainfall

ART
- Bubble painting
- Straw blowing
- Ripple patterns
- Rainbows
- Marbling
- Reflection — Symmetry

MATHS
- Water clocks
- Measuring volumes
- Block graphs (rainfall)
- Oracy — comparing water with other liquids

LANGUAGE
- Imaginative stories 'A day in the life of water'
- Literature
  'Noah and the Flood'
  'Wind in the Willows'
  'Treasure Island'
  'Swallows and Amazons'

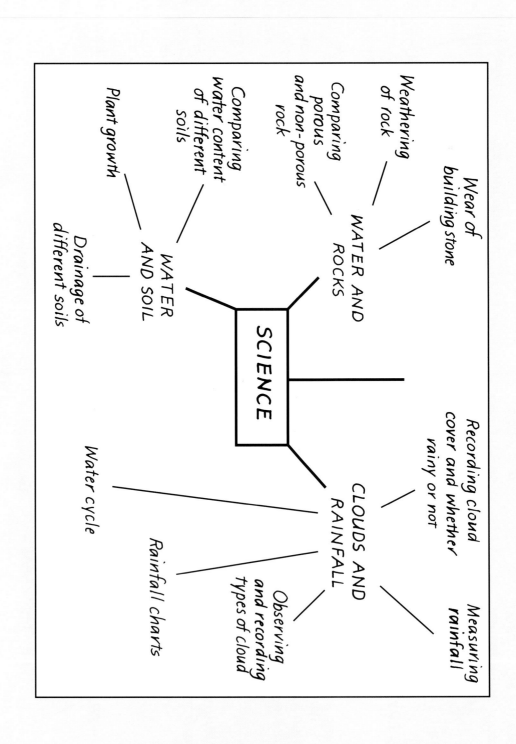

◆ Real life examples of applications of science in the everyday world.

Rocks, soil and weather

A farm in Devon pages 4–5

Purpose: To provide a real-life context for a discussion of land use, to link climate to agriculture and to give children living in rural areas material to which they can relate.
Extension activities: Ask what pesticides are, and why farmers need to use them? There are environmental points to be made about the use of chemical and natural fertilizers - see the text.
Teachers' guide cross-references: Rocks, soil and weather, pages 12, 54; *Living processes*, page 86.

Rocks around the house pages 10–11

Purpose: To introduce rocks in everyday life.
Questions for discussion: Children could list all the places where they see rocks and draw pictures of where they see rocks at home. Discuss children's ideas about where metals come from. (They are found in rocks and mined.)
Teachers' guide cross-references: Rocks, soil and weather, page 55; *Materials*, pages 15, 74–78.

Rocky beginnings pages 14–15

Purpose: To encourage children's enthusiasm for rocks.
Notes: The rock at Lyme Regis is sedimentary rock (defined in the Glossary for *More about rocks, soil and weather*). The rock from volcanoes is igneous rock.
Extension activity: Provide examples of rocks for children to explore.
Teachers' guide cross-references: Rocks, soil and weather, pages 33–4, 40, 58, 87; *Materials*, page 35.

Rocky endings pages 20–21

Purpose: To show that rocks do not last forever, but they undergo 'weathering' erosion.
Extension activities: Look at examples of erosion and landscape change in the news. Children could list the different ways erosion can take place.
Teachers' guide cross-references: Rocks, soil and weather, pages 15, 33–4, 41, 59.

A very human place pages 18–19

Purpose: To provide a starting point for a discussion of the way human activity changes the surface of the earth.
Extension activity: Children could explore the effects of human activity on their local environment, such as buildings, parks, farming and so on.
Teachers' guide cross-reference: Rocks, soil and weather, pages 12–13.

The wind brings the weather pages 2–3

Purpose: To answer the question of why there are different types of weather in Britain and in other parts of the world.
Extension activity: Children could construct their own device to test wind direction, and use it to find out if and how it affects the weather – thus giving themselves an opportunity to test a hypothesis.
Teachers' guide cross-references: Rocks, soil and weather, pages 62 and 70.

The wind and the water pages 6–7

Purpose: To provide opportunities for cross-curricular work in English.
Note: This is a traditional Afro-Caribbean tale from Florida.
Extension activity: Children could make up their own story about the weather and turn it – or the story given here – into a dance.
Teachers' guide cross-references: Rocks, soil and weather, pages 15, 72–3.

The story of sweetcorn pages 8–9

Purpose: To encourage children to consider the way plants grow and the importance of climate to farmers.
Note: Explain that some crops have been bred to create different strains – sometimes naturally, by selective breeding, sometimes by genetic engineering.
Questions for discussion: Why is sweetcorn suited to being grown in America? Why is it less suited to growing in Britain? Can you think of reasons why it can now be grown in Britain? (New strains, climate changes.)
Extension activities: Ask children if they have access to gardens or allotments and if they grow anything to eat – runner beans or tomatoes, for example. Discuss why certain kinds of fruit and vegetables have to be imported at some times of the year, if not always. Why, for example, do we get green beans from Kenya?
Teachers' guide cross-references: Rocks, soil and weather, pages 12–13, 54, 72-3.

Water in the air pages 12–13

Purpose: To convey the concept that the air holds water in the form of visible droplets (mist and steam) and invisible vapour (gas).
Note: Make sure children do not think that liquid water is somehow 'sucked up' into the air.
Questions for discussion: Where have you seen water in the air? (As clouds or rain.) Have you seen mist (water droplets), in a bathroom, for example, or when a kettle boils?
Extension activities: Carry out some experiments on washing and drying. (See the *Using energy* teachers' guide.) Children could list ways of helping things get dry – using a hairdryer, for example.
Teachers' guide cross-references: Rocks, soil and weather, pages 13, 15, 66, 93; *Using energy,* pages 47–49.

What is the weather going to be like? pages 16–17

Purpose: To describe methods of weather forecasting before there were satellites or other modern methods; to give children a starting point for discussion about traditional beliefs about the weather and seasons.
Questions for discussion: How do we tell what the weather is going to be like? What would we do if there were no weather forecast? How can we tell, without using a calendar, what time of year it is?
Teachers' guide cross-reference: Rocks, soil and weather, page 72.

Life in the West Indies pages 22–23

Purpose: To encourage children to think about life in the West Indies and (in the photograph) about how some plants grow in more than one country and climate.
Questions for discussion: What fruit and vegetables do the children recognize? (Sweet potatoes, yams, melon, carrots, pumpkin, oranges, onions.) Which ones could be grown in Britain? (Onions, carrots, tomatoes, spring onions.)
Extension activities: Cross-refer to work in geography. The children could write a story about Velma's day or weekend. Compare the differences and similarities between Britain and the Caribbean. (The verandas, the amount of fruit and vegetables grown, the hurricanes, the clothes people wear – why is there no need for a coat in the rain?) Some children may have relations in the West Indies or have been there themselves and be able to contribute to the discussion. Ask the children to describe a hurricane.
Teachers' guide cross-references: Rocks, soil and weather, pages 12, 15, 72.

More about rocks, soil, weather

Channel tunnel pages 4–5

Purpose: To use a topical context to show rocks under the sea and to explain the importance of knowing about these for an engineering or construction project.
Questions for discussion: How did the two parts of the tunnel meet? Why was the tunnel not built until so many years after it was first planned? (There were political reasons in the 19th century, and the cost was always bound to be huge.)
Extension activity: Find out about the relative costs and travel time taken when travelling through the tunnel or by ferry or by air and discuss the advantages and disadvantages of each journey.
Teachers' guide cross-reference: Rocks, soil and weather, page 47.

Landforms pages 6–7

Purpose: A 'wow' spread, about spectacular land formations.
Note: The pictures show examples of igneous rock formation (the Giant's Causeway) and sedimentary rock formation (the Grand Canyon and Lulworth Cove).
Teachers' guide cross-references: Rocks, soil and weather, pages 33–4, 42-3, 58-9.

Old as the hills pages 8–9

Purpose: A continuation of the previous spread – a 'wow' spread to show that the Earth is made up of layers.
Extension activity: Draw a time line about rock and mountain formation, or make one with a strip of paper.
Teachers' guide cross-references: Rocks, soil and weather, pages 33, 41, 58-9.

Mount Pinatubo pages 12–13

Purpose: To present a news item in a way the class can relate to.
Note: Explain to children what UNICEF is.
Questions for discussion: Who is telling this story? Who would normally write this sort of account? (It would probably be a journalist or some other adult.)
Extension activities: Talk about what a volcano looks like, smells like, etc. Children could write volcano poems, inspired by their feelings and their senses of sight, touch, hearing, smell and so on. Ask children to think about what help the outside world can provide, how people should respond to natural disasters, etc.
Teachers' guide cross-reference: Rocks, soil and weather, pages 34, 43, 83.

Minerals pages 16–17

Purpose: To help children understand what 'mineral' means, (it is in the glossary) and its connection with rocks.
Extension activity: Provide a rock collection for the class to examine. Ask children to list the minerals found on this spread. Get the class to look at different bottles of mineral water and to compare lists of components.
Teachers' guide cross-references: Rocks, soil and weather, pages 56, 82-3.

Toil or soil pages 10–11

Purpose: To counter a major misconception children often have, that plants are made from soil.
Questions for discussion: Does a plant actually need soil to grow? What happens to plants if it does not rain?
Extension activity: Grow plant seeds in a variety of growing media, such cotton wool, paper, soil, water etc.
Teachers' guide cross-references: Rocks, soil and weather, pages 12, 54.

Life in a rotten neighbourhood pages 14–15

Purpose: A discussion spread to help the children think about the structure of soil and the living things found in it.
Extension activity: Bring different kinds of plants and soil into the classroom, and refer to pages 40–1 of this guide for suitable questions to ask the children.
Teacher guide cross-references: Rocks, soil and weather, pages 31, 48-9, 52, 84.

Wet pages 2–3

Purpose: To present the water cycle.
Notes: Water changes from vapour to liquid water to ice and back again.
Extension activities: Children could examine the issue of waste disposal. They could devise and perform a dance or drama on the theme of the water cycle.
Teachers' guide cross-references: Rocks, soil and weather, pages 13, 71, 93; *Materials,* pages 52–3, 99-100.

Sir Gale Force pages 18–19

Purpose: To encourage children to consider the importance of the weather to human activities and history.
Extension activities: Children could try looking at this story from a different perspective – the Spanish one, or that of the English sailors involved. Compare this with other versions of the story which may not mention the weather.
Teachers' guide cross-reference: Rocks, soil and weather, page 72.

Weather woman pages 20–21

Purpose: To describe real person's job – a first-person account of being a weather forecaster.
Note: You could start with a discussion about who really needs to know about the weather – for their work, for example.
Extension activities: Children could list devices used to collect data about weather, and find out how these transmit information. What kind of information are we given in a weather forecast? Using school sensing equipment over a 24-hour period, make a graph showing temperature over a period of time.
Teachers' guide cross-references: Rocks, soil and weather, pages 68–71.

Is the world's climate changing? pages 22–23

Purpose: A discussion spread which gives information about the environment.
Discuss the importance of trees to the landscape and weather systems – children could find out more about this. Discuss why the area of former rainforest in Malaysia been cut down and how this might affect the weather.
Questions for discussion: Children could look at logs or planks of wood for the rings described on page 23.
Teachers' guide cross-reference: Rocks, soil and weather, page 72.

2.6 Planning your science programme in school

The following pages give examples of how two schools have planned their science programme for the whole of Key Stage 2. Planning of this kind helps to provide continuity and progression in children's learning in science. The development of such whole school programmes is discussed more fully in the *Science Co-ordinators' Handbook*.

Each plan covers the requirements for the National Curriculum at Key Stage 2 and shows which themes in the Nuffield Primary Science Teachers' Guides have been used for planning the topic in detail by the class teacher.

Example 1 (page 23)

Based in a semi-rural area this junior school has approximately 170 children on roll. There are no mixed age groups in the school. The plan provides for overlaps in order to provide opportunities for pupils to revisit concepts and build on their previous experience.

The overall curriculum is planned around topics which are history-led in the Autumn term, science-led in the Spring term and geography-led in the Summer term. Therefore, where ever possible cross-curricular links are developed, but if this becomes contrived, then subject specific mini-topics are planned. The programme only shows the Science elements taught each term.

Example 2 (page 24)

This urban school has recently reviewed its science programme in order to help encourage progression in the concepts covered and avoid repetition of the same activities. Teachers asked for guidance but also wanted the flexibility to develop the topics in a way which was appropriate to their own class.

It was also felt that some concepts, not necessarily demanded by the National Curriculum, should be covered e.g. Seasons. Therefore, suitable topics are included in the programme.

The summer term in Year 6 is free to accommodate SATs and to allow teachers time to further develop the interests of children.

Example 1

	AUTUMN TERM	SPRING TERM	SUMMER TERM
YEAR 3	The Earth and beyond/Magnetism	All about me	Service to our homes
Nuffield Primary Science Teachers' Guide	The Earth in Space 3.1, 3.2, 3.3 Electricity and magnetism 3.4	Living processes 3.1, 3.2, 3.3 The variety of life 3.2 Light 3.1	Electricity and magnetism 3.1, 3.2, 3.3 Materials 3.1 Using energy 3.2
Programme of Study †	Sc4:4a, b, c, d; Sc4:2a	Sc2: 1a; 2a, b, e, f; Sc4:3a, d	Sc3:1a, b, c; Sc4:1a, b, c
YEAR 4	Sound and music / Mechanisms	Habitats	Built environment
Nuffield Primary Science Teachers' Guide	Sound and music 3.1, 3.2 Using energy 3.3	The variety of life 3.1 Living processes 3.4 Living things in their environment 3.1, 3.2	Materials 3.2, 3.3 Using energy 3.1
Programme of Study †	Sc4:3e, f, g; Sc4:2d, e	Sc2:1b; 3a, b, c, d; 4a; Sc3:1d	Sc3:1e; 2a, b, c, d
YEAR 5	Electricity/Starting and stopping	Structures	Earth and atmosphere/ Light
Nuffield Primary Science Teachers' Guide	Electricity and magnetism 3.2, 3.3 Forces and movement 3.1, 3.2	Materials 3.1, 3.2, 3.3 Rocks, soil and weather 3.1 The variety of life 3.3	Rocks, soil and weather 3.2 The Earth in Space 3.1, 3.2, 3.3, 3.4 Light 3.2, 3.3
Programme of Study †	Sc4:1a, b, c, d; Sc4:2b, c	Sc3:1b, d; 2f; 3a, b, c, d, e	Sc3:2e; Sc4:4a, b, c, d; Sc4:3a, b, c
YEAR 6	The human body/Keeping healthy	Forces	Our environment
Nuffield Primary Science Teachers' Guide	Living processes 3.2, 3.3 The variety of life 3.2	Forces and movement 3.1, 3.2, 3.3, 3.4 Electricity and magnetism 3.4 Using energy 3.3	Living things in their environment 3.2, 3.3, 3.4
Programme of Study †	Sc2:2c, d, g, h	Sc4:2a, b, c, d, e, f, g, h	Sc2:5a, b, c, d, e

† For the purposes of these charts the references to sections of the
Programme of Study have been abbreviated as follows:
Sc2 = Life Processes and Living Things
Sc3 = Materials and their Properties
Sc4 = Physical Processes

Example 2

	AUTUMN TERM		SPRING TERM		SUMMER TERM	
YEAR 3	Earth and time	Reflections and shadows	What's under our feet?	Moving things	Variety of life	Habitats
Nuffield Primary Science Teachers' Guide	The Earth in Space 3.1, 3.2	Light 3.2	Rocks, soil and weather 3.1 Living things in their environment 3.3	Forces and movement 3.1	The variety of life 3.1	Living things in their environment 3.1
Programme of Study †	Sc4:4a, b, c, d	Sc4:3a, b, c	Sc2:5e; Sc3:1d	Sc4:2a, b, c, d, e	Sc2:1a, b; 4a	Sc2:5a, b
YEAR 4	Frictional forces	Hot and cold	Materials and their properties	Sounds	Growing	Electricity
Nuffield Primary Science Teachers' Guide	Forces and movement 3.2	Using energy 3.1	Materials 3.1	Sound and music 3.1	Living processes 3.1, 3.4	Electricity and magnetism 3.1, 3.2, 3.3
Programme of Study †	Sc4:2b, c, f, g, h	Sc3:2b, c	Sc3:1a, b, e	Sc4:3e, f	Sc2:3a, b, c, d	Sc3:1c; Sc4:1a, b, c
YEAR 5	The Earth in the Solar System	Weather and its effects	Feeding relationships	Individual variation	Light sources	Sounds travelling
Nuffield Primary Science Teachers' Guides	The Earth in Space 3.1, 3.2, 3.3	Rocks, soil and weather 3.1, 3.2	Living things in their environment 3.2, 3.3	The variety of life 3.2	Light 3.1	Sound and music 3.2
Programme of Study †	Sc4:c, d	Sc3:1d, 2e	Sc2:5c, d, e	Sc2:4a; 5a	Sc4:3a, b, c, d	Sc4:3e, f, g
YEAR 6	Forces and movement	Living processes	Electricity	Materials		
Nuffield Primary Science Teachers' Guide	Forces and movement 3.3, 3.4	Living processes 3.2, 3.3	Electricity and magnetism 3.1, 3.2, 3.3	Materials 3.2, 3.3		
Programme of Study †	Sc4:2d, e, f, g, h	Sc2:2a, b, c, d, e, f, g, h	Sc4:1c, d	Sc3:2a, b, d, f; 3a, b, c, d, e		

2.7 Resources

Full use should be made of the school grounds or nearby open spaces.

The precise nature of the resources needed at any time will, of course, depend upon the ideas that the children have and the methods of testing that they devise. However, the following list provides a general guide to the resources needed to carry out the investigations shown in this book.

Transparent plastic bottles
Funnels (cut from plastic bottles)
Transparent jars (with screwtop lids)
Thermometers
Hand lenses
Tweezers
Gloves
Spade, trowel
Transparent plastic bags (and other containers for soil collection)
Soil samples from different places in Britain
Samples of rock
Pictures of rock formations, rocky areas, famous rocks, gemstones etc.
Books, videos, pamphlets and posters giving information about rocks, soil and the weather.

2.8 Warnings

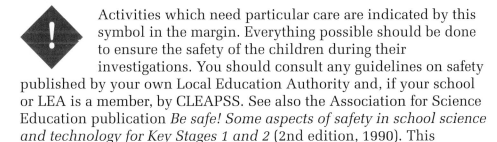 Activities which need particular care are indicated by this symbol in the margin. Everything possible should be done to ensure the safety of the children during their investigations. You should consult any guidelines on safety published by your own Local Education Authority and, if your school or LEA is a member, by CLEAPSS. See also the Association for Science Education publication *Be safe! Some aspects of safety in school science and technology for Key Stages 1 and 2* (2nd edition, 1990). This contains more detailed advice than can be included here.

Fieldwork and visits must be carefully organized and supervized – follow your school or LEA guidelines.

Children must not look directly at the Sun during studies of the weather.

Children should not attempt rock chipping. If it is to be done at all it should be carried out only by a teacher using a geology hammer and eye protection. Children should not be nearby at the time.

Take care when examining soils, as they can be contaminated by treatment with fertilizers and pesticides. Soil fouled by dogs or cats may transmit toxocara worms which can cause blindness. Children should have tetanus injections before handling soil.

It is illegal to bring soil into this country from abroad.

CHAPTER 3

Exploring rocks, soil and weather

Theme organizer
ROCKS, SOIL AND WEATHER

ROCKS AND SOILS
3.1

There is a wide variety of rocks and soils.

The Earth's crust – its outer shell – is made up of rock, which is sometimes covered at the surface by soil or water.

Soil is formed from very small bits of rock together with material from the decay of living things, particularly plants.

*The characteristics of a soil depend upon the nature of the rock from which it was formed and on the processes involved in its formation.

Various factors, for example wind, rain and living things, cause rock to change and disintegrate into small pieces, which can be carried away by wind and water.

*The Earth's crust consists of rigid slabs called plates which can move, resulting in earthquakes, volcanic activity and other changes to the surface of the Earth.

*Rock belongs to one of three basic types – igneous, sedimentary and metamorphic – depending on the way it was formed.

WEATHER
3.2

Weather conditions change from day to day and show patterns which are related to seasonal changes.

Weather conditions and seasonal changes have significant effects on the environment and influence the behaviour of all living things.

*Weather changes are the result of the heating effects of the Sun and the resulting movement of air in the atmosphere.

(*Asterisks indicate ideas which will be developed more fully in later key stages.)

Rocks and soils

KEY IDEAS

◆ There is a wide variety of rocks and soils.

◆ The Earth's crust – its outer shell – is made up of rock, which is sometimes covered at the surface by soil or water.

◆ Various factors, for example wind, rain and living things, cause rock to change and disintegrate into small pieces, which can be carried away by wind and water.

◆ Soil is formed from very small bits of rock together with material from the decay of living things, particularly plants.

◆ *Rock belongs to one of three basic types – igneous, sedimentary and metamorphic – depending on the way it was formed.

◆ *The characteristics of a soil depend upon the nature of the rock from which it was formed and on the processes involved in its formation.

◆ *The Earth's crust consists of rigid slabs called plates which can move, resulting in earthquakes, volcanic activity and other changes to the surface of the Earth.

(*Asterisks indicate ideas which will be developed more fully in later key stages.)

A LOOK AT
rocks and soils

The crust of the Earth is rock covered in some places by water and in other places by soil. Deep in the Earth the rock is liquid, but this is encircled by a relatively thin layer of solid rock. There are different kinds of rock. They have not always existed but were formed in different ways.

Over long periods of time, rock can break down. Water can penetrate it, freeze and so split the rock by its expansion as it changes to ice. Water can also attack some kinds of rock directly and change it into a form that crumbles more easily. The roots of plants can penetrate cracks in rock and exert such pressure that the rock splits. All these effects break the rock into smaller pieces.

Water can also dissolve some rocks, and water and wind can wear it away by friction. These can also carry fragments of rock to other places. The appearance of the Earth's surface is therefore gradually changed over a long period of time. Some rocks are more resistant than others. Less resistant parts of exposed rocks are worn down faster, leaving the more resistant parts projecting more prominently.

When plants and other things living in and on the small bits of crumbled rock die, their remains decay and become mixed up with the rock pieces. Over a long time the tiny bits of rock and the decayed material of once living things become soil. Soil also contains air and water. Both water draining through the soil and creatures living in it can alter the soil.

The Earth's land surface is often covered by soil, hiding the rock that lies underneath. Different kinds of rock produce different kinds of soil. Soils differ in their colour, texture and the relative proportions of the various bits they contain.

Rock can also move as a whole. Huge sections of the Earth's crust, called plates, drift slowly across the surface at a rate of a few centimetres per year. Where plates collide, the rock buckles, folding to form mountains. Where plates move apart the result may be a rift valley; this can also lead to mountain building as liquid rock moves upwards through the weakened surface. Volcanic activity and earthquakes take place chiefly at or near the boundaries of different plates.

AREAS FOR INVESTIGATION

◆ Different kinds of soil.

◆ What is under the ground?

◆ Rocks and how they can change.

◆ Different landforms.

The study of rocks may be linked with work in the *Materials* teachers' guide. The study of soils may be linked with the work on decay in the *Living things in their environment* teachers' guide.

Finding out children's ideas

■ STARTER ACTIVITIES

1 What is under our feet?

Take children on to the playground or a patch of grass and ask them to imagine digging down through it:

 What do you expect to find as you go down?

Encourage them to go down as deep (in their thoughts) as they can. They could show what they think by means of annotated drawings.

Talk to the children about their drawings. You might ask them:

 Tell me about your drawing.
What have you drawn there?
How far down does that go?
Is there anything under that?

If the children use any terms such as 'subsoil' or 'humus', you might find out what meaning they attach to these by asking:

 What do you mean by that?

If two drawings – one for 'under the playground' and one for 'under the grass' – are made, it is possible to see whether children have consistent ideas about what is under the ground.

2 Soil

a What is soil?

Ask children to bring in samples of soil from their own gardens. Children should be warned to take soil only under adult supervision so that they do not handle soil that has been contaminated. They should use gloves if possible and wash their hands after handling soil.

Display the soil samples in polythene bags or jars, and if possible add other soils from outside the area, for variety.

Let the children look at the samples under hand lenses. Ask them:

Q *How are the soils the same?*
How are the soils different from each other?
What do you think makes them the same/different?

Responses to these questions might be recorded in a log book kept beside the display.

Individual records could be made by children drawing a picture of one sample and writing some sentences in response to the question:

Q *What do you think soil is?*

Further questions put to individuals or asked during group discussions will draw out more ideas about soil and its origins.

Q *What is soil like?*
What do you think soil is made of?
How do you think soil got to be like this?
Where does soil come from in the first place?
Can soil change at all?
What does soil do?

b Different soils

The intention of this activity is to find out what children consider to be soil. Use a number of clear containers, each with a sample inside it. These might include sandy and chalky soil, peat, sand and tiny stones. Ask:

 Which of these would you call soil?

For those that have been chosen, you could then ask:

 What makes you call these soil?

For those not selected, you might ask:

 What makes you say that this isn't soil?

The activity could be conducted in groups, with the teacher or a child noting down the ideas that are mentioned.

c Soil and plant growth

This activity may be linked to work on plant growth in *Living processes.*

Use two different looking soil samples. Ask:

 How could you find out which one is better for plants to grow in?

Children should think about how to do it rather than conduct an actual test at this stage. They might give an oral or written account of what they would do. Other questions might be:

 What do you think makes a soil good for plants to grow in?
How might you make a soil better for plants to grow in?
Where do you think you would find the best soil for plants to grow in?

(This activity is continued in the 'Helping children to develop their ideas' section, on page 53.)

3 Rock

a Where is rock found?

One starting point is to ask the children:

 What do you think of when I say the word 'rock'?

Get them to draw pictures showing where they think rock can be found. Further questions to ask include:

> *Do you think there is rock under every place?*
> *How do you think the rock got there?*

Responses to these questions could be written down or made in discussion.

b What is rock like?

One way of introducing this question is to have a number of samples of rock – small and large pieces, round and jagged pieces, hard and soft rocks, a lump of concrete, some sand and perhaps a picture of a very large rock outcrop. You might then ask:

> *Which of these would you call rock?*
> *What makes you call these ones rock?*
> *What makes you say this one isn't rock?*

4 Weathering

Ask children to draw a piece of rock and then to show on the drawing how they think this piece might change over a long period of time.

If possible, show children pieces of exposed and worn stonework on buildings.

Let them draw pictures of what they have seen, and give their ideas in response to:

> *Has it always looked like this?*
> *What was it like before?*
> *What do you think made it change?*

Children could either say what they think or add some words to the drawings they have made. Another possibility is for children to draw a series of pictures to show how and why they think a piece of stone (a tombstone, for example) might have changed over time.

Piece of rock now | How it might be in the future

5 Landforms and landscapes

Work on landforms is best undertaken on a field trip. There may be prominent landforms in the vicinity of the school. Children may also be able to draw on their own experiences of hills, mountains, flat areas, valleys, cliffs, coastlines, and so on. You could ask them to relate some of those experiences and

CHECK SCHOOL POLICY ON VISITS. SOME PARTICULARLY INTERESTING PLACES, SUCH AS QUARRIES, ARE ALSO PARTICULARLY DANGEROUS

ask questions like:

 Do you think (the mountains) have always been there?
How do you think they were formed?
Will they always stay like that?

For features and events children are less likely to have experienced, such as volcanoes and earthquakes, you may be able to show pictures or slides to stimulate their thinking. Then ask questions like:

 What do you think volcanoes are?
What do you think causes earthquakes?

Children's ideas

What is under our feet?

The following pictures were drawn by children to show what they thought was beneath their feet. Some children's drawings show only the top surface of the Earth while other children's show that they have ideas about the whole structure. Some penetrate as far as Australia!

In the first picture the soil is shown as containing a number of different things, while in the second picture the existence of different layers has been recognized. In neither case has the bedrock beneath the soil been drawn.

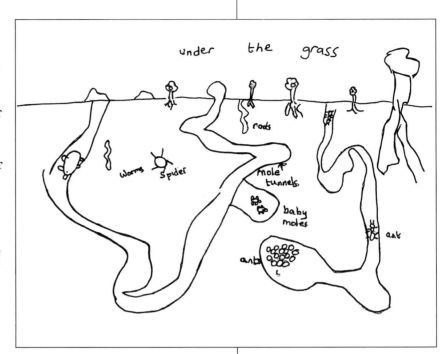

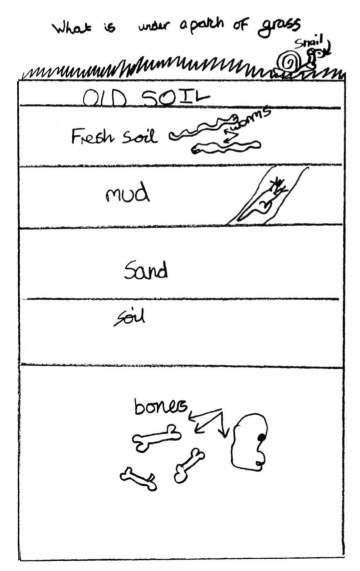

This picture reveals a number of interesting features. First, water has been shown. Some children have the idea that there are layers of water, occasionally referred to as an underground sea. Second, a layer of rock has been drawn. However, this does not appear to be envisaged as a continuous band of rock but rather a layer containing many individual and separate rocks. Third, this child – like many others – has continued to the centre of the Earth. The centre has been drawn with a curved line.

The picture below incorporates curvature into all the layers. The child has used the term 'crust' without indicating an accurate understanding of it. It is also mixed with an idiosyncratic 'egg' model of the Earth. It is not clear, without further questioning, how literally the child takes this idea.

The picture opposite shows a more detailed awareness of the Earth's structure. The distance given, though not accurate, is of the right order of magnitude. It reveals a more developed concept of distance than is shown by most children, who tend to underestimate substantially the magnitudes involved.

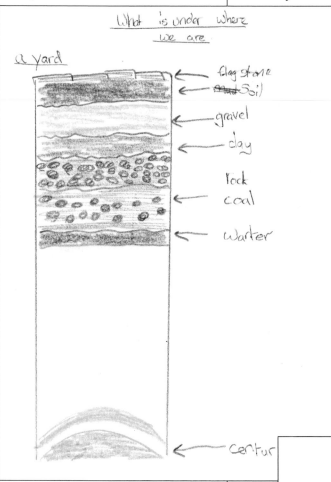

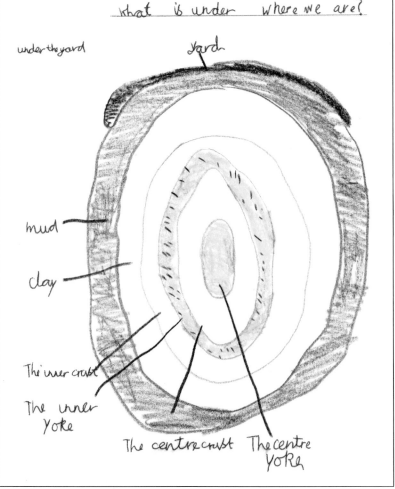

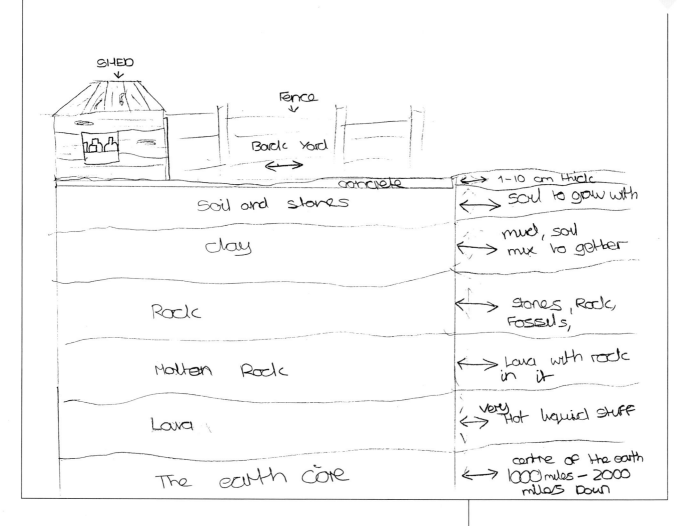

what is under the yard?

SHED
Fence
Back yard
concrete

Soil and stones — 1-10 cm thick, soil to grow with
clay — mud, soil mix together
Rock — stones, Rock, Fossils,
Molten Rock — Lava with rock in it
Lava — very Hot liquid stuff
The earth core — centre of the earth 1000 miles – 2000 miles Down

Soil

Soil is strongly associated in most children's minds with growing things. It is often difficult for them to conceive of plants growing without soil. When it comes to finding out which of two soils is better for growing plants in, children often make remarks based on the appearance or feel of the soils – though one of the following also suggests a practical test.

How would you Find out which soil is For Plants to Grow in! The dark brown one is because it is will absorb More water than the other and the other Soil is to hard.

I would feel with my fingers it ʌ and squash it. If it is fine its rubbish if its chunky its good soil

Their idea is that you can tell the 'goodness' of a soil by looking or feeling. Even if they cannot do this themselves, they could call on an expert to make it fair.

to do a fair test I would take them to a garden Center and ask Some one who knows abt doout soil and plants. or go to a libaray and get a book.

Of course, a great deal *can* be told about soil by looking and feeling, particularly by an expert. Appearances can be deceptive, however, and some children ignore them and simply call for a test.

Plant a seed in each pot, put them both in sunlight, and water and take care of each one and see which one grows the best.

As this example indicates, children do not always control variables carefully or indicate how the dependent variable – best growth – will be determined.

Many children take soil to be a collection of little bits of a certain size and colour. They are strongly influenced by the soils they see around them, particularly the often enriched topsoil of a garden. Thus, many children in a non-chalk area did not accept a chalky soil as soil because, they said, 'It's too light in colour' or 'The bits are too big'. The tendency is to see soil as the little dark brown bits – larger pieces of rock and bits of visible decaying matter are in the soil but not regarded as part of it.

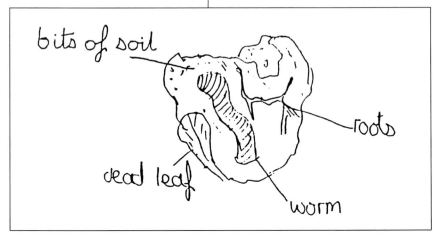

The bits of soil are not often associated by children with rock. A reason given for this is that 'Rock is hard and soil is soft'. In view of this, it is not surprising that children's ideas about the origins of soil do not often include rock.

A common idea is that soil has always existed, but in a different place. People get it from somewhere else for their gardens, and farmers bring it in for their fields. In contrast, here are some comments by different children who have the idea that soil has not always been around.

> *It's from the old rubbish you put down. When the worms get it, they chew it up and it comes out into this soil. It goes in front and comes out of the back as soil.*
>
> *Soil is rock which has ground into soil.*
>
> *It's like been a plant over millions of years and then it's just got ground underground and turned into soil.*
>
> *It's ground down from rocks when the water washes up on it. It keeps doing it and gradually it gets turned into sand and soil.*

Rock

Children associate rock with the places where it is readily seen because it is not covered by soil.

We can find rocks When you are Gardening and when you climb up mountins. and when you go to the beach you find rocks in the rock pools. and they are Jaged and couler full and gold and silver.

Jaged and gold   silver

Children seem less aware of layers of rock lying underneath the soil and rarely refer to them. Where they do refer to rock under the soil it is generally as isolated pieces. Here, however, is one child who is clearly aware of rock layers.

You find rocks in different layers of earth
You find different kinds of rocks in different layers

It is also uncommon for children to refer to the use of rock in, for example, building stone.

Here are some further ideas about rock.

> Rocks are hard things and if you throw them they hurt.

> Rocks are like stones but they are bigger.

 Rocks are jagjed and rufe

> Rocks are sometimes lumps of sement or claye.

Children commonly think of rocks as being above a certain size and distinguish them from stones, which are smaller. Some children refer to jagged shape as an important feature of rocks, while others accept rounded shapes as rock. The final comment above shows no differentiation between man-made material and rock which occurs naturally.

The tendency to think of rock as hard may lead children to think of it as being permanent and unchanging. In consequence, many children assume that rock has been here for ever, so there is no need to consider its origin.

A few children, however, do express ideas about rock formation, such as the cooling of molten lava or the sticking together of smaller particles. Here is one example.

> Rocks are big peices of mud that has dried through the ages.

Weathering and landforms

The perceived hardness of rock can be a barrier to an awareness of the breakdown and movement of rock. The following illustrations show some different ideas about the wearing away of rock in the built environment.

People and weather both cause change.

Rain causes change.

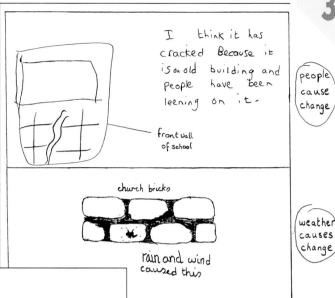

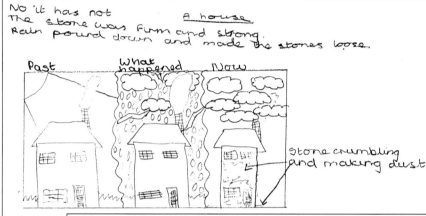

(*Above*) Stone gets dirty with age – wear is not mentioned.

(*Right*) Severe weather causes change.

(*Left*) Stone gets old.

Some children have ideas about the erosion of rock in the natural environment.

Rocks are bits of mountains or hills that have fallen down.

but if a rock is all jaggerd
the it folls of a cliff in to
will sea and come out oguin it
be smoth

I think that hills were made by an earthquake when the earth shook the contents just rolled on top of each other I do not think that they have always been there.
I think that valleys were formed by water. The water must of made the soil shrink somehow.

Many children suggest that valleys, hills and mountains have always been there, but often acknowledge that they may change. In this example the child links the formation of mountains to earthquakes but has a different reason for valley formation.

Some children recognize the effects of human activity on the landscape.

2. They were made from a rubbish tip and it grew over the top.
3. The valleys formed by water running through the hills and it has come away and it has came into a valley.
4. The hills wont stay there were people have been walking it will come away and it will turn into a mound.

Most children show an awareness of earthquakes and volcanoes, and some can give quite sophisticated explanations of their causes.

Volcanoes are a kind of hollow mountains. that have a long shaft that leads to the earths crust. Every once in a while the magma at the bottom erupts and the lava over fills the volcanoe causing it to spill over the top. An earthquake is caused by the hot liquid that is in the earths core. the liquid gives off gases and the pressure of the gas that is trying to get out causes an earthquake so the ground shakes.

Helping children to develop their ideas

The chart opposite shows how you can help children to develop their ideas from starting points which have given rise to different ideas.

The centre rectangles contain starter questions.

The surrounding 'thought bubbles' contain the sorts of ideas expressed by children.

The further ring of rectangles contains questions posed by teachers in response to the ideas expressed by the children. These questions are meant to prompt children to think about their ideas.

The outer ovals indicate ways in which the children might respond to the teacher's questions.

Some of the shapes have been left blank, as a sign that other ideas may be encountered and other ways of helping children to develop their ideas may be tried.

1 What is under our feet?

For some children, the question 'What's under the ground?' takes them into soil only. Others are able to go deeper to consider the whole structure of the Earth. Without taking children beyond their comprehension, encourage them to get more evidence in relation to their ideas about what is under the ground.

You may have asked children to make drawings when you were first trying to find out their ideas. You could go on by asking them to compare their drawings in groups, and to consider the different ideas they have expressed. Ask them:

  What evidence can you find that the things you have shown might be there?
Could there be anything under the bottom thing you have shown? How can you find out?

A combination of first-hand experience and use of secondary sources will supply evidence against which children can evaluate their ideas.

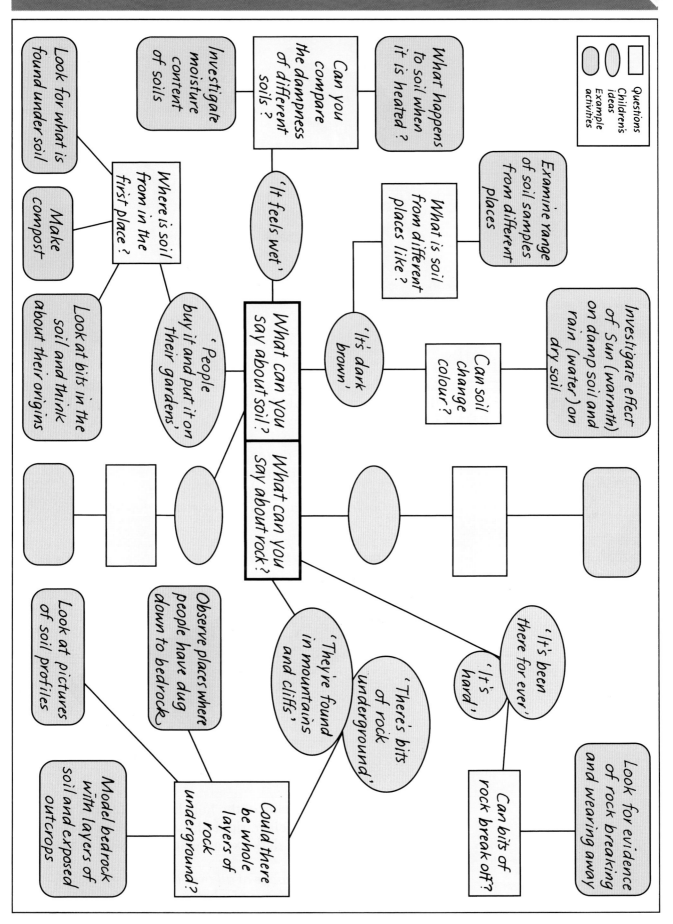

Legend:
- Questions (rectangle)
- Children's ideas (oval)
- Example activities (rounded rectangle)

Questions and activities:

- Look for what is found under soil
- Investigate moisture content of soils
- Can you compare the dampness of different soils?
- What happens to soil when it is heated?
- Examine range of soil samples from different places
- Make compost
- Where is soil from in the first place?
- What is soil from different places like?
- Investigate effect of Sun (warmth) on damp soil and rain (water) on dry soil
- Look at bits in the soil and think about their origins
- 'It feels wet'
- 'People buy it and put it on their gardens'
- 'It's dark brown'
- Can soil change colour?
- **What can you say about soil?**
- **What can you say about rock?**
- Observe places where people have dug down to bedrock
- 'They're found in mountains and cliffs'
- 'There's bits of rock underground'
- 'It's been there for ever'
- 'It's hard'
- Look at pictures of soil profiles
- Model bedrock with layers of soil and exposed outcrops
- Could there be whole layers of rock underground?
- Can bits of rock break off?
- Look for evidence of rock breaking and wearing away

a Digging a hole

Let children dig into the soil to look for the things they have drawn. The hole should be about 60 cm deep. A carefully dug hole with straight sides will show a soil profile. Ask:

 How far down do the plant roots go?
Are there any changes in colour?
Do there seem to be layers in the soil?
Do the bits change in size as you go down?

AT 1 RECORDING

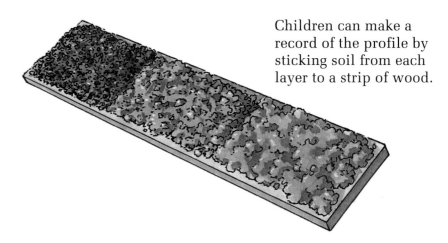

Children can make a record of the profile by sticking soil from each layer to a strip of wood.

Further use could be made of the hole by covering the vertical section with a sheet of clear, rigid plastic. Put black plastic over the hole to keep it dark except when you want to use it.

 Does the soil change at all over time?
Is there any evidence of what can change it?

t SOIL CREATURES AND WATER CAUSE CHANGES IN SOIL

b Looking at other holes

Take opportunities for children to look at other profiles – for example:

- holes in roads for pipe laying, etc.;
- recently made road cuttings;
- the banks of streams, rivers and drainage ditches, if the layers are not concealed by vegetation.

Study these profiles and pictures of others, and make comparisons.

Q *What features do the profiles have in common?*
How do the profiles differ?
What do you think makes them the same/different?

The profiles may show underlying rock. First-hand experience of rock layers can be obtained if a hole can be dug deep enough. A visit to a quarry would show the soil and the rock that lies underneath it.

Another starting-point for discussion about what is underground would be the 'Channel Tunnel' pages in *More about rocks, soil and weather*.

c Is there rock underground?

Many children believe that there is rock underground, but often they consider it to be in the form of individual rocks rather than continuous layers.

Set up a debate by asking:

Q *Is there rock underground?*
What do you think it is like?
Is there rock under every place?
Do you think there could be rock under here which reaches all the way to (some distant place)?

Encourage the children to search for evidence of their ideas. They could find out about mines, drilling, caves and tunnels. Books, photographs, newspapers and videos may all be useful sources of information here.

Some children may be able to model the Earth's surface. Plaster, papier-mâché or some other material could be used to represent rock; the surface should be uneven. Soil could then be sprinkled over the surface so that any projecting plaster is seen to represent mountains, cliffs, and other outcrops of what is a continuous band of rock.

 SAFETY ON VISITS, ESPECIALLY TO WORK SITES AND RIVERS. CHECK SCHOOL POLICY

 THIS MAY NOT BE PERMITTED OR SUITABLE FOR YOUNG CHILDREN

 pb

 t THE EARTH IS MAINLY ROCK

AT 1 COMMUNICATING

 e

 t THE SOIL IS ONLY A SHALLOW SURFACE COVERING

d Going deeper

If children appear ready to take on new ideas about the deeper parts of the Earth's structure, you could discuss their meanings of words such as 'crust', 'mantle' and 'core' with them. (See Chapter 5 'Background science.) Children could think of other examples of the use of these words in order to develop an appreciation of why the words are used in the context of the Earth's structure. Ask questions such as:

Q *What are these parts inside the Earth like?*
How do we know that they are there?

These questions could both provoke discussion and lead to a search for further information.

Some children might be able to make a model of a section of the Earth's sphere in Plasticine of various colours. They could cut it in half to see the layers. Alternatively, you could get children to cut an apple in half, draw it and mark the parts which correspond to the crust, core and mantle of the Earth. Ask them to consider how well the skin represents the crust, the flesh the mantle, and the core the Earth's core.

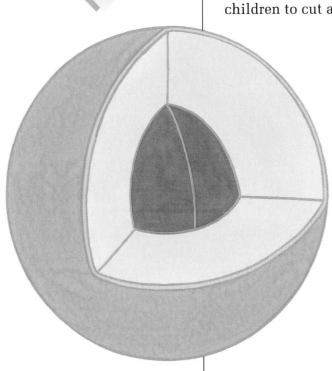

You can ask the children to consider whether these models show the depths of the various layers accurately. If children have found values for the depths in secondary sources, they might use these to draw a cross section to scale. This could be a large co-operative effort stretching along a whole wall of the classroom. Help the children to think about what some of the depths mean.

Q *Can you compare the depths to the distances of journeys you have made yourself?*

2 Soil

a A closer look at soil

Encourage children to reconsider their ideas about what soil is and what it contains by getting them to look more carefully at soil samples. They could work in groups to separate the samples by hand into all the different kinds of bits they can find. Hand lenses will be useful here. If possible they should wear gloves. Ask them to name the sorted bits and display what they have done.

See if they can suggest other ways of separating and sorting the soil. They could perhaps add water to see which bits float, or add water and shake to see how the different bits settle. They could use sieves, meshes and fabrics to separate bits of different sizes.

 t THE PARTS OF THE SOIL THAT COME FROM LIVING THINGS FLOAT

 e

More about rocks, soil and weather describes different types of soil and how they are formed. This could be used as part of a discussion comparing different soils.

 pb

b Origins of soil

Can the children trace the various bits they have found back to their origins? You might ask:

 How did those bits get there?

SOME PARTS OF THE SOIL COME FROM LIVING THINGS THAT DIE AND DECAY

If some bits are recognized as coming from plants, you can help children to make a study of what happens to plant material that falls and is covered by soil. A compost heap could be examined, or even set up.

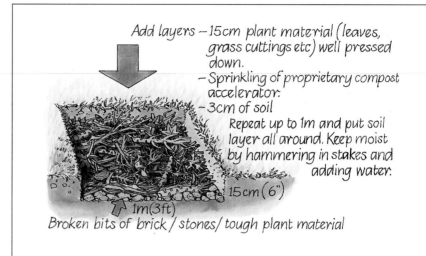

Add layers –15cm plant material (leaves, grass cuttings etc) well pressed down.
– Sprinkling of proprietary compost accelerator.
– 3cm of soil
Repeat up to 1m and put soil layer all around. Keep moist by hammering in stakes and adding water.
15cm (6")
1m (3ft)
Broken bits of brick / stones / tough plant material

t SOME PARTS OF SOIL ARE BITS OF ROCK

It is more difficult to understand that some of the bits in soil come from rock and that they are, in fact, little bits of rock. You could ask:

 Where do the bits that haven't come from plants or animals come from?
Could they have come from rock?

 e

Ask the children whether they can find or think of any evidence for their response. They could study the little bits carefully with a hand lens, or even a microscope. Ask:

 Do they look as if they could have come off rock?

Pieces that have been separated by using water could be examined after they have dried out.

The children could also study rock samples. Ask:

 Are there any little bits next to the samples?
Can you make the rock crumble?
Have you seen any examples of crumbled or split rock?

 YOU SHOULD WEAR SAFETY GLASSES IF YOU TRY TO FLAKE PIECES OFF ROCK. CHILDREN SHOULD NOT BE NEARBY AT THE TIME. CHILDREN MUST NOT FLAKE ROCK

This would be a chance to help children develop their ideas about the wearing away of rock (see page 57).

c Soil and rock types

Another indication of where soil comes from is given by looking at the soils associated with various rock types. Children may have limited experience of different soil types. Some may think of soil as only one thing – dark brown garden topsoil.

 OBSERVING

Encourage children to form a more general idea of soil by giving them a variety of soil types to examine - sandy, chalky and peaty, for example. You can ask them to separate the soils in the way previously described (page 48-49). If possible, provide samples of the kind of rock from which the soils have derived.

Q *What similarity is there between the sandy soil and sandstone?*
How is chalky soil like the rock chalk? How is it different?
Why is peaty soil such a dark colour? Does it have any bits of rock in it?

Such questions can help children develop their ideas about the relationship between rocks and soils. The studies of soil profiles mentioned in the activities about 'What is under our feet' (page 44) are also relevant here. Children could use a computer database to enter information about the different soils they look at. They might record colour, texture, presence of visible bits from plants, any creatures present, where the soil was found, how moist it seems, and so on. They could then carry out a search for soils with certain features.

d More things in soil

Water
Some children may have the idea that soil is dried mud. Ask them to think about how they can find out whether soil contains water, and if so how much. They could compare different soils.

Encourage children to make the comparison as fair as they can, without telling them what to do. In a fair test, an equal weight of each soil should be taken, and the soils should be dried out in the same way before being reweighed.

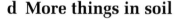

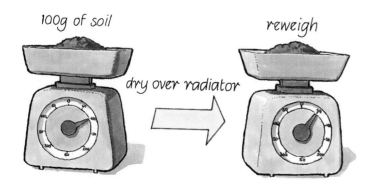

Some dry-looking soil may reveal that there is moisture in it. You or they might raise questions such as:

Q *Can different soils hold different amounts of water?*
Does water drain through some soils more quickly than others?

THE COLOUR OF SOIL IS RELATED TO THAT OF THE ROCK IT CAME FROM; PEAT COMES ALMOST WHOLLY FROM DECAYING MATTER

AT 1

AT 1

PLANNING AND CARRYING OUT FAIR TESTS

WATER DRAINS THROUGH SOME SOILS AND TENDS TO BE HELD IN OTHERS

The picture below shows the apparatus used by one group of children investigating such questions. They were asked to make predictions before the test.

Air

Children are less likely to mention air as part of soil; they often take soil to be the solid bits only. You might discuss with groups whether they think there is anything between the soil 'bits'.

Q *Are those spaces?*
If so, does anything fill the spaces?

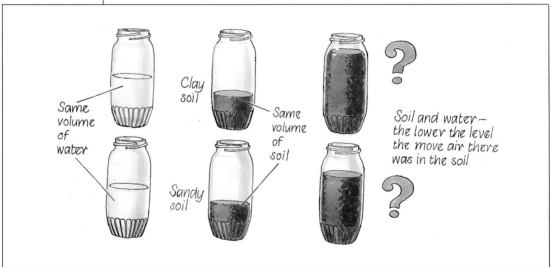

AT 1   MEASURING

t   WATER TAKES THE PLACE OF THE AIR BETWEEN THE SOIL PARTICLES

The children could then predict which of a number of samples would have more spaces, and so more air in them. You could include gravel among samples of sandy and clay soil, for example. The picture above shows one way of testing the predictions fairly.

Living things

Children may also have referred to creatures that live in soil. They may have ideas about what the creatures do, what they feed on and which part of the soil they are found in. Encourage them to consider their ideas against evidence provided by first-hand observation, if possible, and by information from secondary sources.

A wormery is a good device for first-hand observation. You can get children to set up one like that shown on the next page.

More about rocks, soil and weather refers to animals and fungi in the soil. This could help children to consider what they do as soil forms.

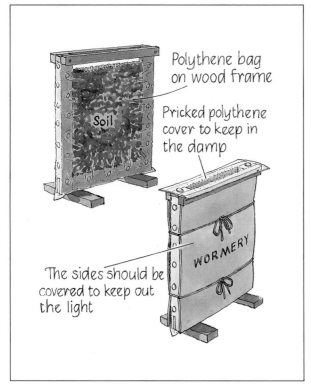

Polythene bag on wood frame

Pricked polythene cover to keep in the damp

Soil

WORMERY

The sides should be covered to keep out the light

> **t** LIVING THINGS CAN CAUSE MOVEMENT OF SOIL

> **AT 1** GENERAL

it

e Soil and plant growth *(continuation of starter activity)*

Ask children to say how they would find out which of two soils is better for plants to grow in. Get them to plan what they would do, working in groups. Prompt them by suitable questions to be as rigorous as they can.

The agreed plan could be compiled with a word processor.

If they say they can tell by how the soil looks, ask:

Q *Can you really be sure by looking?*

If they do not specify how to tell which plant is growing best, ask:

Q *How will you know which plant is growing better?*

If they choose to plant only one type of seed in each soil, ask:

Q *What if your seed doesn't grow?*
What if one seed is better than another?

If they do not use equal amounts of soil and treat them in the same ways, ask:

Q *How will you make your comparison fair?*

After planning, children should carry out the investigation.

Get them to consider carefully what they are doing, and to review their plans critically as they go along.

 SOME SOILS SUIT CERTAIN PLANTS

Children who have experience of gardening may be able to consider whether a particular soil will always be better for all plants. You might also ask:

Q *How might you make soil better for plants to grow in?*

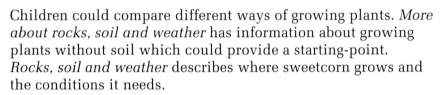 **pb**

Children could compare different ways of growing plants. *More about rocks, soil and weather* has information about growing plants without soil which could provide a starting-point. *Rocks, soil and weather* describes where sweetcorn grows and the conditions it needs.

Some practical work may be done on this subject; much information can also be gained about what grows well in certain kinds of soil from gardening and nature books, and by talking to professional gardeners.

pb

Rocks, soil and weather considers how a farmer looks after the soil on his farm. This could be used for information and further discussion. The same book shows some of the ways in which people control the types of plants and animals that live in different places.

f Is soil the same everywhere?

Children could carry out a soil survey by collecting soil samples from different places in Britain. Ask the children to design their survey.

 AT 1 DESIGNING AN INVESTIGATION

Q *Where is the soil to come from?*
What tests are going to be done on the samples?
How will the findings be recorded and presented?

One class asked teachers and parents to bring a sample of soil back from the places they had gone on holiday (in Britain). Another took advantage of a parent who was a lorry driver – he and his friends brought soil back from the places they went to.

Children could map where the soil samples come from and discuss their findings.

 Is the soil from different places the same?
How is the soil different?
What do you think makes it different?
Could the type of rock in an area affect the soil?
Is the soil from a garden different from other places?

3 Rocks and landscape

The previous two sections have referred to the idea of rock as continuous layers and the relationship between rock and soil. This section considers the nature of rock itself, including how it breaks down and its effect on the landscape.

a What is rock?

Set up a collage display of children's pictures showing their ideas of where rock might be found. Help children to extend their ideas by asking them to add to the collage pictures, drawings or photographs of things made from rock. They might include statues, gravestones, gemstones, pastry-making slabs, kerb and paving stones, fireplaces, and various other parts of buildings from doorsteps to roofing slates.

Rocks, soil and weather could be used to help children discuss the types of rock found in the home.

Discuss the examples.

 Are the rocks all the same?
In what ways are the rocks the same/different?
Are (paving stones) made from natural rock or man-made materials?

This might be followed by a visit to a town centre to survey the use of stone as a building material. (This work can be linked to that suggested in the *Materials* teachers' guide). You could prepare a 'stone trail'. See how many different kinds of building stone the children recognize. They could make sketches of buildings noting any natural stone used, and man-made 'stone' such as concrete, tiles and bricks.

Help children to think of rock as a kind of material. Give them a set of materials, perhaps building materials. Ask them to classify them into rock and man-made material. Sort them

IT IS ILLEGAL TO BRING SOIL FROM ABROAD INTO BRITAIN

AT 1 COMMUNICATING

AT 1 OBSERVING. RECORDING

pb

CHECK SCHOOL POLICY ON VISITS

e

again into rock, plastic, metal, wood and ceramics, if these are available.

Try to broaden children's experience of the variety of rocks. One way to do this is by visiting a stonemason's yard. Not only can different types of materials be seen there but children can also see the various techniques for cutting and shaping rock. They may be able to see that some kinds of rock cut more easily than others and that some rock crumbles relatively easily. This may cause a reconsideration of their ideas about the hardness and indestructibility of rock. Churchyards may also show a variety of types of material used for gravestones.

Build up a collection of rock samples at school. Children should contribute to it. Some unusual or striking examples would add to the interest. Pictures and posters could also be looked at, and perhaps displayed with the collection.

Rocks, soil and weather gives some examples of different rocks and where they can be found.

Get the children to sort the rocks in different ways. They might start by choosing simple criteria such as colour or shape. They could also look at them with a hand lens and sort them into those in which particles can be seen without the lens, those in which particles can be seen only with the lens, and those in which no particles can be seen. Information about the rock samples might be recorded on a database.

Some children may want to find out more about comparing and identifying rocks. They could find ways of doing this in secondary sources. One question that might arise from their experiences is:

! CHECK SCHOOL POLICY ON VISITS: INDUSTRIAL PREMISES ARE DANGEROUS PLACES

e

pb

t ROCKS ARE MADE OF SMALL PARTICLES OF MINERALS

it

! CHILDREN MUST NOT CHIP OFF ROCK SAMPLES; IF YOU WISH TO DO SO, WEAR SAFETY GLASSES. ANY CHILDREN NEARBY MUST ALSO BE WEARING GLASSES

t THE SCRATCH TEST IS USED TO IDENTIFY PURE SAMPLES OF MINERALS RATHER THAN ROCKS

pb

Q *We say things are 'rock hard' – are all rocks equally hard?*

These drawings show some ways in which children might tackle the problem.

More about rocks, soil and weather considers minerals and provides a starting-point for a discussion about what the word 'mineral' means.

b Weathering

Experience of rock being cut shows that it can break down. What evidence can children find for the disintegration of rock in the built environment?

Ask them to look for and draw examples of wear to stonework and man-made materials:

◆ worn and cracked paving stones;
◆ worn steps;
◆ corners of walls worn away;
◆ potholes in the playground.

Ask them also to think of evidence for the breaking down of rock in the natural environment:

◆ chunks of rock with cracks or splits;
◆ screes below steep slopes;
◆ rockfall underneath cliffs.

Encourage children to discuss why they think the original rock changed.

 What kinds of thing wear away rock?
Do you think rock breaks into big bits or small bits?

Children may mention 'weather' or 'weathering'. It is important to establish what they mean by the terms, which they may equate with strong storms rather than a gradual process.

 When is rock worn away by the weather?
Do you think it could be happening all the time?
Is the rock worn away slowly or quickly?

If children mention water or rain, can they explain the idea?

 How can water split rock?
How does water get into rock in the first place?

These two questions may lead children to investigate whether different rocks can soak up water and the consequent effects of freezing. The effects are seen more easily if you use Plaster of Paris rather than real rock, but even this will need to be put into and taken out of a freezer about twelve times.

The following illustrations suggest possible investigations.

pb

Rocks, soil and weather and *More about rocks, soil and weather* both provide examples of rocks being worn away which can be used for information and discussion.

c Landforms and landscapes

 CHECK SCHOOL POLICY ON VISITS

A field trip extends children's first-hand observation of landforms and the landscape. Children may have ideas about what various landforms are like, and these can be compared with actual observation or with information presented in secondary sources. They may also have ideas about the causes of the formations they see. Here you will need to help children to consider their ideas in relation to those given by secondary sources.

e

You could get children to model what happens when water falls on broken rock with an arrangement such as this one.

A similar activity can be done with soil to show how it can be washed away by water.

The fact that wind can also move tiny bits of rocks and soil can be demonstrated by putting sticky strips in various exposed places out of doors and examining them later. You may need to discuss whether things children find stuck to the strips are bits of rock and soil.

Children could also investigate how steeply different materials can be heaped, by piling them into mounds.

The formation of fold mountains can be modelled by using layers of coloured Plasticine to represent rock strata.

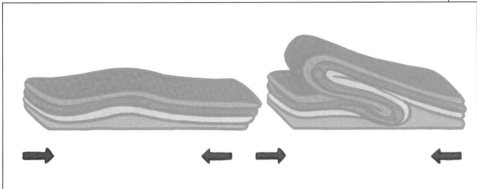

One difficulty with these models is that they show in a short time processes which occur over thousands of years. Suggestions as to how children can be helped to develop notions of very long times are given in *The variety of life* teachers' guide. These refer to life-forming processes, but some geological processes occur over even longer periods; others, such as weathering and erosion, take less time though often more than children can easily envisage.

Earthquakes and volcanoes sometimes produce changes in the Earth's surface much more quickly. Ask children to plot the sites of these events on a world map and to look for any patterns in where they lie.

Encourage children to discuss their ideas about why there is a pattern and to follow this up with a search among secondary sources for other ideas.

Q *How do these ideas explain what actually happens?*

More about rocks, soil and weather gives examples of the formation of mountains and other landforms which could be used as a stimulus for discussion. It also gives an eye-witness account of the eruption of Mount Pinatubo in 1991.

EARTHQUAKES AND VOLCANOES HAPPEN MOST FREQUENTLY ALONG THE LINES WHERE PLATES MEET

Weather

AREAS FOR INVESTIGATION

◆ Observations of the types, changes and patterns of the weather over time.

◆ Measurements and records of various weather factors.

◆ The effects of the weather on the environment.

KEY IDEAS

◆ Weather conditions change from day to day and show patterns which are related to seasonal changes.

◆ Weather conditions and seasonal changes have significant effects on the environment and influence the behaviour of all living things.

◆ *Weather changes are the result of the heating effects of the Sun and the resulting movement of air in the atmosphere.

(*Asterisks indicate ideas which will be developed more fully in later key stages.)

A LOOK AT
weather

The Earth is a rocky planet surrounded by an atmosphere of air. Changes in the atmosphere, mostly in the lower levels, result in changes in the weather. Air is all around us. It extends upwards some distance from the Earth, thinning out as you go up. Moving air is wind. Winds vary in both speed (or force, or strength) and direction. Speed is measured by a device which is spun by the wind. Direction is measured with a vane which points to where the wind is coming from. A knowledge of speed is important because of the damaging effect of high winds. A knowledge of direction can help in the prediction of likely weather. For example, westerly winds in Britain often bring rain.

Clouds contain tiny droplets of water and crystals of ice. These particles may merge and become heavy enough to fall as rain, hail or snow. Clouds form when warm air rises. Warm air can hold more moisture as invisible vapour than cold air. The rising air cools and some of its water vapour becomes liquid water. There is a movement of water from the Earth's surface into the air and back again.

Rainfall can be measured by catching rain in a container and measuring the height of the water collected. It can vary a great deal from place to place, even within a small area.

Temperatures vary from one part of the world to another. Average temperatures are broadly influenced by the height of the Sun's path in the sky. Other factors are important, such as nearness to the sea, height above sea level and, on a day to day basis, cloud cover and where the wind is blowing from.

Weather forecasting uses detailed measurements of existing conditions and awareness of weather patterns to make predictions.

Finding out children's ideas
■ STARTER ACTIVITIES

1 Observation and causes of weather changes

Draw children's attention to the weather and suggest that they record what it is like. Try to avoid feeding words and ideas to them at this stage; encourage them to use their own terms.

The initial discussion can be followed by asking the children:

 Can you make a record of the weather on the next 4 or 5 days?

A sheet of paper divided into columns headed 'Monday', 'Tuesday', etc. is a convenient recording chart. The children should record the features they feel are relevant in their own way – by writing, drawing or symbols. Older children might be encouraged to devise and use their own symbols.

Discuss the records with the children. Ask questions such as:

 Why did you record (these features)?
What does this symbol mean?
Why did you use this symbol to represent (this feature)?

Having clarified the records made by the children, try to find out their ideas on what causes changes in the weather. Ask:

 What do you think makes the weather change from (say) sunny to (say) rainy?
What do you think makes it rainy/foggy/sunny etc.?
What do you think the weather is like in different places in the world?
What is the weather like at different times of the year?

An annotated sequence of drawings would be an appropriate way for children to make their responses.

2 Weather forecasting

Ask the children to watch some television weather forecasts. Use a class discussion in order find out the children's ideas. Ask questions such as:

 What is the forecaster doing?
How do these people know what the weather is like?
How do they know what the weather is going to be like tomorrow/next week?
What do you think the various symbols mean?

You may find it convenient to record the responses of the children on a chart similar to those shown on pages 45 and 69 – that is, put the question in the middle and cluster responses around it. This will help in planning activities to develop ideas.

3 Effects of the weather

Encourage children to think about the effects of the weather rather than the weather itself. Annotated drawings could be used to record ideas in response to questions such as:

 What happens to things when it is windy/raining/sunny? What do you think would happen if you could change the weather so that it was very windy/very hot and sunny/raining all the time? Do you think the weather can make places different?

This activity could be linked to a creative writing task. Ask the children to imagine that they are able to control the weather and to write a story about what happened when they changed the weather.

Discuss the drawings and stories with children:

 Why do you think windy/rainy/sunny weather would do that? What do you think is the worst/best thing that is caused by the weather?

Children's ideas

Weather observations and records

Children are usually able to make some kind of observations about weather conditions and to record them in some way. The use of symbols appears to develop gradually from more pictorial representation. In the weather record that follows, the child has drawn sky scenes but it is as much words as pictures that tell the story. Indeed, almost identical pictures have been drawn to portray 'cold' and 'warmish'.

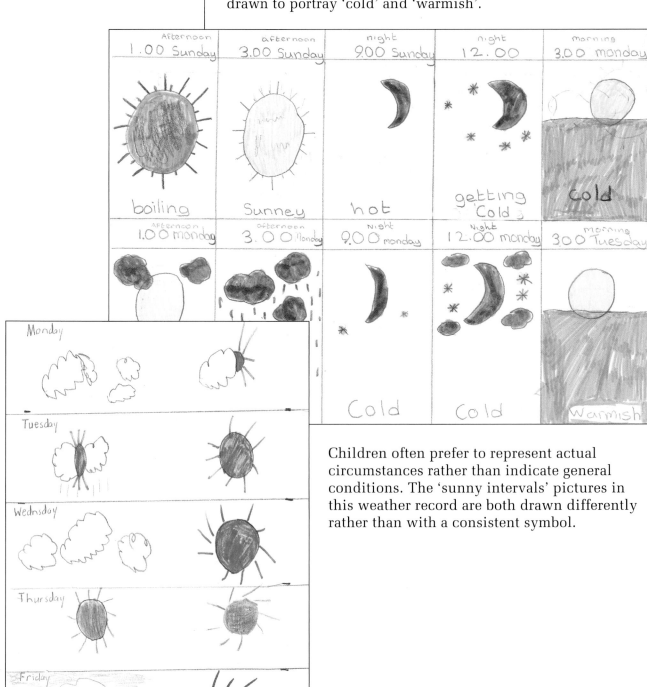

Children often prefer to represent actual circumstances rather than indicate general conditions. The 'sunny intervals' pictures in this weather record are both drawn differently rather than with a consistent symbol.

Reasons for weather

Here is one child's comment about how a forecaster can tell us about the future weather. It indicates that each country gets its weather in turn – the same weather?

> He will Know because county's that have time ahead of us send a note what is is Like

While it is true that frontal systems may result in belts of rain and temperature moving in particular directions, the reference to 'time ahead of us' indicates a fixed direction. Another child proposed the mechanism for this arrival of weather in a fixed order – the rotation of the Earth. The weather is fixed in the heavens and the Earth rotates to receive it in turn.

The same child has ideas about the formation of clouds.

because the earth is turning there may be no clouds in front of England but then it may turn and there may be clouds in front of England.

water is sucked up from the sea into the clouds when the clouds are full the water is let out. and come down as rain

The active 'sucking up' of water into the clouds makes it sounds as if the cloud has an existence independent of the water it contains. Children associate clouds with rain but it can be difficult to interpret whether they realize that clouds consist of water. The following drawings show some further ideas about the clouds, rain and the Earth.

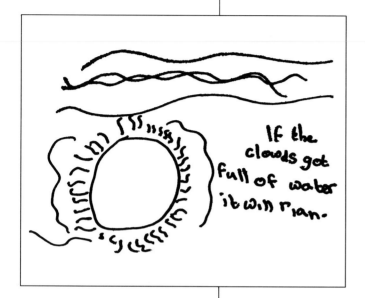

If the clouds get full of water it will rian.

The clouds move because the Earth moves.

Forecasting weather

Many children recognize that satellites have a role in forecasting the weather, although they are often unaware of what the satellites observe and measure, and how this helps predictions.

<u>My weather forcast</u>

He was telling us what it would be like today. I think the have satellites that tell them.

the satellites go throgh to this big machine.

Others are aware that instruments are used.

The man can tell what the weaser will be licke by using special instruments.

It is not clear whether these 'special instruments' are for measuring aspects of the weather. Others do mention specific instruments.

> he's got a weather cock to tell him what the weather will be like

Although the above example may make the forecasters appear archaic, it is true that measuring wind direction is a sound basis for making predictions.

Other ideas may resemble folklore, as in the following example. Once again, however, cloud type can be a useful indicator of future weather.

> he can tell by the clouds

This same child is aware of the importance of using information from a number of places (although she may believe that countries receive the same weather in turn).

> I think he knows what the weath is like because he get the megges from other contrys

Helping children to develop their ideas

The chart opposite shows how you can help children to develop their ideas from starting points which have given rise to different ideas.

The centre rectangle contains a starter question.

The surrounding 'thought bubbles' contain the sorts of ideas expressed by children.

The further ring of rectangles contains questions posed by teachers in response to the ideas expressed by the children. These questions are meant to prompt children to think about their ideas.

The outer ovals indicate ways in which the children might respond to the teacher's questions.

Some of the shapes have been left blank, as a sign that other ideas may be encountered and other ways of helping children to develop their ideas may be tried.

1 A weather station

Much of the work of developing ideas will be based on making records of the weather, followed by sorting and discussing the data collected.

Setting up a weather station provides opportunities for:

◆ designing and making a range of devices for measuring the different aspects of the weather (links with design and technology);

◆ making measurements – length/height, volume, time – with emphasis on the need for a standard method of collecting data so that results can be compared fairly;

◆ looking for patterns and interpreting data and making predictions;

◆ use of secondary data sources for tracing records of past weather conditions;

◆ recording and representing data in various ways, using graphs, bar charts, maps and symbols.

Organization may be a problem with this activity because it is difficult for every child or group to record every aspect of the weather. Therefore a class discussion to decide the aspects to be studied could be followed by a different group of children taking responsibility for each feature of the weather.

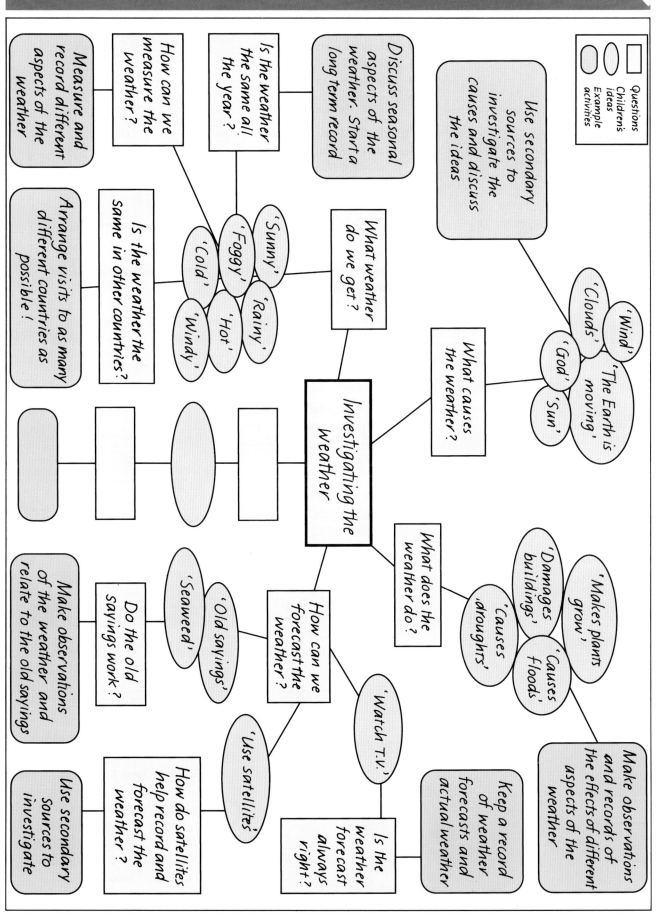

Questions
Children's ideas
Example activities

Use secondary sources to investigate the causes and discuss the ideas

Discuss seasonal aspects of the weather. Start a long term record

Is the weather the same all the year?

How can we measure the weather?

Measure and record different aspects of the weather

'Sunny'
'Foggy'
'Cold'
'Rainy'
'Windy'
'Hot'

What weather do we get?

Is the weather the same in other countries?

Arrange visits to as many different countries as possible!

Investigating the weather

What causes the weather?

'Wind'
'Clouds'
'The Earth is moving'
'God'
'Sun'

What does the weather do?

'Damages buildings'
'Makes plants grow'
'Causes droughts'
'Causes floods'

Make observations and records of the effects of different aspects of the weather

Keep a record of weather forecasts and actual weather

Is the weather forecast always right?

How can we forecast the weather?

'Seaweed'
'Old sayings'
'Watch T.V.'
'Use satellites'

Do the old sayings work?

Make observations of the weather and relate to the old sayings

How do satellites help record and forecast the weather?

Use secondary sources to investigate

Some aspects of weather which might be covered include the following.

a Sunshine can be recorded in terms of
- hours of sunshine
- shadows
- intensity
- frequency.

Q *Is the sunshine always the same during the day? Which part of the year has the most sunshine?*

! DO NOT LOOK DIRECTLY AT THE SUN

b Temperature can be measured (a maximum–minimum thermometer is most helpful).

Q *Does the temperature change during the day? At what time of the day is the temperature highest? Is it the same every day?*

c Wind speed and direction can be measured, and the prevailing direction worked out.

Q *Does the wind always come from the same direction? Does the wind always blow at the same strength? Is the wind speed the same in all places?*

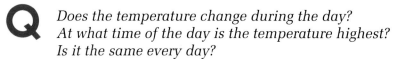

pb

Rocks, soil and weather looks at how the wind influences the weather.

d Clouds – cover, shape, colour, movement – can be recorded in symbols or in writing.

Q *What happens to the clouds during the day? Do we get particular types of clouds with different kinds of weather?*

Rocks, soil and weather can be used for a discussion of clouds.

e   Rain can be measured with a gauge, and frequency and an estimate of drop size recorded.

Q *When it rains, is it always exactly the same?*
Does rain fall evenly on the ground?

More about rocks, soil and weather has a large picture of the water cycle.

If possible, arrange a visit to a local weather station so the children can compare their own records with the official ones, and see the instruments that are used to make various measurements.

Active use of secondary sources (books, old records and maps, video) should be encouraged to extend the data available and to find out other ways of measuring the weather. In particular, the use of satellites and computers could be investigated.

More about rocks, soil and weather has an account of how weather forecasts are prepared for television. This can be used as the start of a discussion.

2 Discussion

Children should present their findings in a variety of ways (charts, pictures, writing, models) so that everyone can see all the work. Discussion of the findings is important, both as a class and in groups. Use particular questions to help focus the discussion. Some examples might be:

Q *Is it always colder when the wind blows?*
Does it always rain when it is cloudy?
Is it always hot when the sun shines?
What is the weather like when it is dark?

What do you think is going to happen to the clouds we can see today?
What has happened to the clouds we saw yesterday?
What happens to the Sun at the end of the day?

Ideally the measurements of weather conditions should be made at different times of the year so that comparisons can be made.

 Why do you think weather is different at different times of the year?

Rocks, soil and weather points out the problems that Stone Age farmers had in forecasting the weather at different times of the year; it also encourages children to consider folklore today.

Encourage children to compare their findings with those for other parts of the world. Make a collection of information given in newspapers and/or travel brochures. Ask:

 What do you think makes the weather different in other parts of the world?

Rocks, soil and weather has a short account about how the climate affects life in the West Indies. Children could compare this with other places. *More about rocks, soil and weather* provides a stimulus for discussion about possible changes in the world's climate.

3 Effects of the weather

Children should look for evidence of the effects of different weather conditions. Wind is probably the most obvious, but the effects of rain, sun, ice and snow can also be seen if observations are made at the appropriate time. Consider particular activities that are affected by the weather such as:

- ◆ sports;
- ◆ outdoor pursuits (climbing, sailing, canoeing, potholing);
- ◆ holidays;
- ◆ occupations (gardeners, builders, farmers);
- ◆ agriculture, in different parts of the world as well as this country.

More about rocks, soil and weather suggests that the weather was an important factor in the defeat of the Spanish Armada. You could go on to discuss other such historical events with the children – such as Napoleon's retreat from Moscow, defeated by 'General Winter'. Tchaikovsky's '1812' overture describes the story well!

Secondary sources can provide information, but this is an opportunity for children to collect information from other people. They could act as reporters and interview parents and family about the worst weather they have experienced and the effect it had on them. These interviews could be recorded on tape and played back for other children to listen to and discuss.

Rocks, soil and weather gives a story about the wind and the water. Children might use this as a stimulus for their own creative writing, or for research into legends and stories about the weather.

CHAPTER 4

Assessment

4.1 Introduction

You will have been assessing your children's ideas and skills by using the activities in this teachers' guide. This on-going, formative assessment is essentially part of teaching since what you find is immediately used in suggesting the next steps to help the children's progress. But this information can also be brought together and summarized for purposes of recording and reporting progress. This summary of performance has to be in terms of National Curriculum level descriptions at the end of the key stages, and some schools keep records in terms of levels at other times.

This chapter helps you summarize the information you have from children's work in terms of level descriptions. Examples of work relating to the theme of this guide are discussed and features which indicate activity at a certain level are pointed out to show what to look for in your pupils' work as evidence of achievement at one level or another. It is necessary, however, to look across the full range of work, and not judge from any single event or piece of work.

There are two sets of examples provided. The first is the assessment of skills in the context of the activities related to the concepts covered in this guide. The second deals with the development of these concepts.

4.2 Assessment of skills (AT1)

Things to look for when pupils are investigating rocks, soil and weather, as indicating progress from level 2 to level 5:

Level 2: Making suggestions as well as responding to others' suggestions about how to find things out about or compare rocks, soil and weather. Using equipment, such as magnifying glasses or a balance for weighing, to make observations. Recording what they find and comparing it with what they expected.

Level 3: Saying what they expect to happen when something is changed and suggesting ways of collecting information to test their predictions. Carrying out fair tests, knowing why they are fair, and making measurements. Recording what they find in a variety of ways; noticing any patterns in it.

Level 4: Making predictions which guide the planning of fair tests. Using suitable equipment and making adequate and relevant observations. Using tables and charts to record measurements and other observations. Interpreting, drawing conclusions and attempting to relate findings to scientific knowledge.

Level 5: Planning controlled investigations of predictions which are based on scientific knowledge. Using equipment carefully, repeating observations as necessary. Using line graphs to record and help interpretation; considering findings in relation to scientific knowledge.

The teacher had decided that children should investigate the characteristics of rocks and soils in the school grounds. The children had been encouraged to bring rocks into the classroom. A display of rocks was made which included sandstone, chalk and granite. The children handled the rocks on display and by asking questions the teacher encouraged the children to discuss their observations.

What do you notice about the rocks?
Can you describe some of the ways in which the rocks are the same and some of the ways in which they differ?

Many of the children mentioned the properties of the rocks in the display and the teacher encouraged them to test their ideas. (For safety they were not allowed to chip pieces off the rocks).

You find rocks on beaches and other places like parks near diggs and in gardens sometimes on the street's and roads on mountains beside lakes and rivers, Some rocks look like crystal and some look like black blob or a spot they are hard some of them sparkle they are not soft you can make fire with it and if you hit someone with it would hurt.

Riyaz

Riyaz's work showed that he made observations of the rocks and introduced some information from his knowledge of rocks. There is no evidence of responding to suggestions to find things out and this work has not reached level 2.

Some children noticed that some rocks were harder than others and wanted to find a way of finding which was the hardest.

Stuart's careful observation of sandstone shows in his drawing and in discussion with the teacher he suggested that sandstone would hold more water than a grey stone in the collection. Peter also thought that the stones would absorb different amounts of water and proceeded to test this.

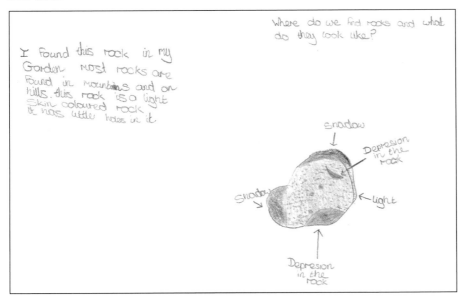

I found this rock in my Garden most rocks are found in mountains and on hills. this rock is a light skin coloured rock it has little holes in it

Where do we find rocks and what do they look like?

shadow
Depression in the rock
light
Shadow
Depression in the rock

Stuart

Peter's account indicates that he made relevant measurements of the mass of the stones before and after soaking. He made his test fair by placing the stones in water for the same time and ensuring that no surface water was measured. He has used the measurements to draw conclusions in relation to the prediction he made. Although the masses of the two stones were not the same, and thus he has not really compared like with like, he has compared the water absorbed by these two particular pieces of stone in a fair manner. Whether or not he realises that he cannot use these results to say that sandstone absorbs more water than the grey stone might be clarified in discussion. His work appears to be at level 3. He could be encouraged to link the observations of the stone to its water absorption in attempting to explain his findings and thus make progress towards level 4.

Experiment to see if stones soak up water

We chose 2 different stones, one was hard and grey, the other sandstone.
We thought the sandstone might hold water.

We weighed the stones.

STONE   WEIGHT (dry)
GREY   112g

WON'T
SANDSTONE
WILL   120g

We placed the stones in water for 5 minutes.
We carefully dried the stones and weighed them again.

STONE   WEIGHT   Results after soaking
GREY   113g

SANDSTONE   122g

They both absorbed water but the one that we thought would take in water absorbed more.

Peter

4.3 Assessment of children's understanding (Part of AT3)

Aspects of work relating to rocks, soil and weather indicating level 2 to level 5:

Level 2: Comparing different rocks and soils in terms of observable features and grouping them accordingly. Describing common weather conditions.

Level 3: Awareness that rocks and other building materials are changed by weathering processes such as heating, cooling, squashing, stretching and abrasion. Knowing that water can exist as solid and as liquid and that the change can be reversed.

Level 4: Knowing how rocks and soils are formed and that particles of different sizes and kinds in soil can be separated by sieving or sedimentation. Knowing the meaning of melting, freezing, evaporation and condensation and that these are reversible changes.

Level 5: Knowing the conditions in which freezing, melting, condensation and evaporation take place and the part played by condensation and evaporation in the water cycle.

Louise's writing and drawing shows that she has grouped the rocks according to whether they have speckles or not. She is also aware that while there are ways in which the rocks in each group are similar, there are also ways in which they differ. Comparing and grouping rocks in this kind of way indicates work at level 2.

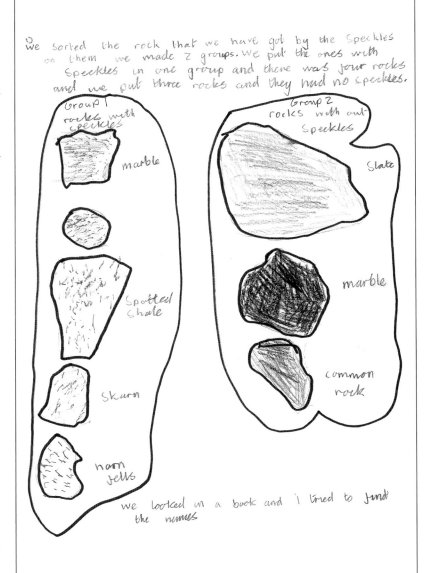

Louise

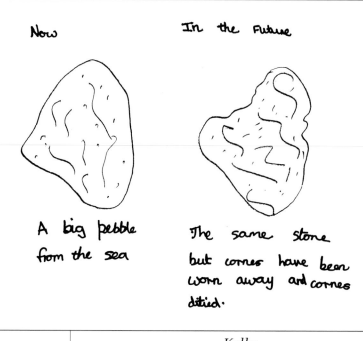

Now

In the Future

A big pebble from the sea

The same stone but corners have been worn away and corners ditied.

Kelly

Kelly mentions that she expects the corners of the stone would be worn away in the future. She is aware of the changes that might happen to the rock, but does not attempt any explanation of how the rock might be worn away, which would provide evidence of understanding. Her ideas about how the weathering might take place would need to be discussed to confirm work at level 3.

Kim identified some of the effects of weathering and, in discussion, explained that it takes place gradually, either because of the weather or because of stones rubbing together. Kim's ability to explain how weathering takes place reveals some understanding of the process of weathering and demonstrates that this aspect of his work is at level 3.

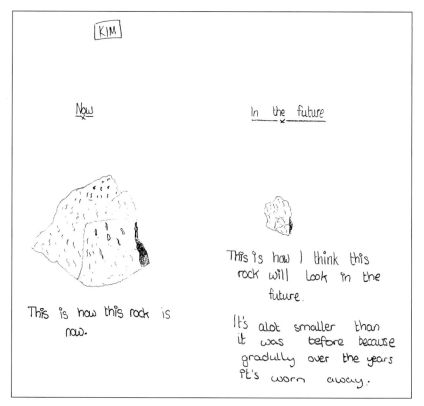

KIM

Now
x

In the future
x

This is how this rock is now.

This is how I think this rock will look in the future.

It's a lot smaller than it was before because gradually over the years it's worn away.

Kim

Rosie's work indicates some detailed knowledge of how weathering takes place. Like Kim, she is aware that changes caused by weathering take place slowly. She goes further, however, in describing how the bits of rock are washed into the sea, causing further erosion. This indicates a firm understanding at level 3. Discussion may reveal what Rosie knows about what happens to the fragments of rock which are washed away and the extent to which she is aware, as Rachel appears to be, that these may form sediments and eventually be incorporated into rocks or soil.

Rachel describes the effects of weathering, explaining that as the rock becomes worn, pieces break off to form sand and soil. Her description reveals an awareness of the formation of soil, together with an understanding that soils can be transported by different weather conditions and the sea. These aspects of this work reflect achievement at level 4.

Rosie

Very slowly the wind rain and sun has worn the stone away. The wind has done it by blowing on it and made parts of the stone weak and eventully break of bit by bit. The rain gets into the cracks the sun make. The Sun keeps shining on the stone and makes the stone hot. When the stone gets hot it expand and that is when it cracks. The rain then gets into the cracks and wears more of the stone away. If the stone is near the sea or a river then when the tide comes in it takes the stone with it and it gets tossed about whitch wears the stone away too.

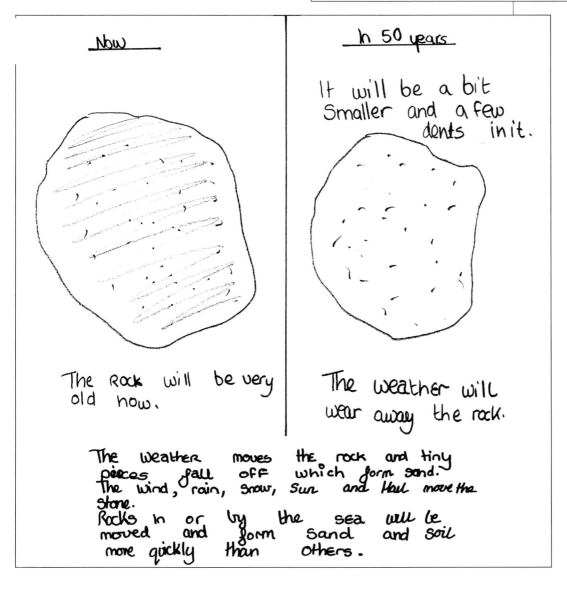

Now

The Rock will be very old now.

In 50 years

It will be a bit Smaller and a few dents in it.

The weather will wear away the rock.

The weather moves the rock and tiny pieces fall off which form sand. The wind, rain, snow, sun and Hail move the stone.
Rocks in or by the sea will be moved and form Sand and soil more quickly than others.

Rachel

In David's drawing, the Sun is depicted as a source of heat, yet his writing does not indicate an appreciation of how changes in temperature influence the water cycle. He mentions that the sea is evaporating, but he does not include any suggestion of water changing state. Indeed, the water seems to be collected only as water in clouds. David does not suggest any reason why the water should fall from the clouds. So he has not demonstrated a clear understanding of the physical processes involved. David's comments and drawing suggest his work has not yet reached level 5.

Peter's drawing and explanation, unlike David's, pay some attention to the effects of changes in temperature. He mentions that heat causes the water to evaporate, and that as the temperature falls, rainfall goes back to the sea. Peter also points out that this is a continuous process. Further questioning could probe the extent of Peter's understanding. However, explanation of the water cycle in terms of the effects of temperature change indicates that this aspect of his work is closer to level 5 than David's.

The water in the sea is evaporating and then The water changes into a cloud and then the wind blows it and then the rain comes out of the cloud

David

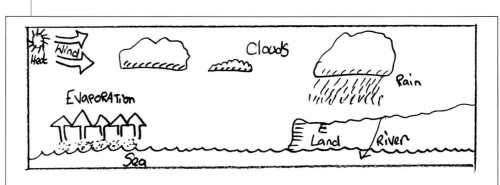

Water Evaportion by the heat of the Sun When it is cold the rain falls and goes back into the Sea. It carryes on like that every time it rains. It is called a Water cycle. It goes roond in a cirick. Also Wind moves clouds across the land

Peter

CHAPTER 5 — Background science

Rocks and soils

Origin and structure of the Earth

There is substantial scientific evidence that the Earth formed about 4500 million years ago. The diagram below gives some idea of the time scale involved. However, it is difficult, if not impossible, to appreciate times of millions of years.

The Earth's history

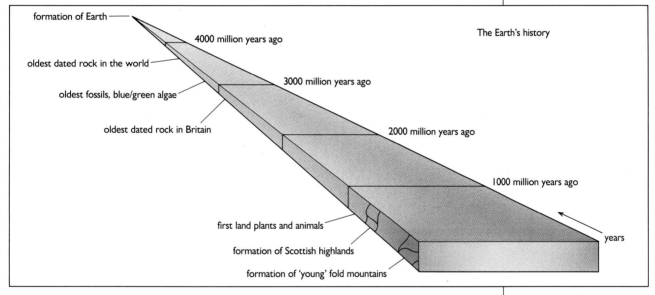

formation of Earth

4000 million years ago

oldest dated rock in the world

The Earth's history

3000 million years ago

oldest fossils, blue/green algae

oldest dated rock in Britain

2000 million years ago

1000 million years ago

first land plants and animals

formation of Scottish highlands

formation of 'young' fold mountains

years

The Earth's structure

The Earth formed as a cloud of gas swirling around the Sun, then cooled into a hot liquid ball. As cooling continued, the liquid material on the outside of the ball began to solidify and a crust formed over the Earth's surface. Even now, billions of years later, the relatively cool surface of rocks, water and abundant life hides a very hot interior, some of it liquid. One kilometre below ground in a mine a noticeable rise in temperature can be felt. At 200 kilometres, the temperature is something like 1500 °C; that is, dull red heat.

The structure of the inside of the Earth has been worked out by studying earthquake shock waves. Waves of a certain type travel through solids but hardly at all through liquids, and so the places they reach (or do not reach) as they travel through the Earth

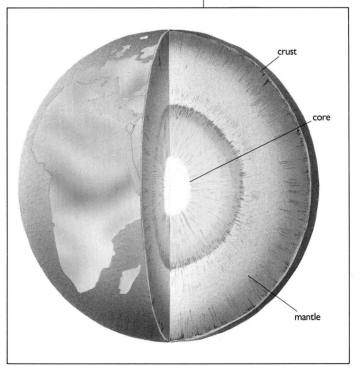

crust

core

mantle

from a quake in a given place indicate that a region in the centre of the Earth must be liquid. Further analysis of shock waves suggests that the interior of the Earth consists of layers, as shown in the diagram.

The outer layer, the **crust**, varies in thickness. The average thickness under the oceans is 6 km (about 4 miles), while under the continents it is 40 km (25 miles). The crust lies on top of a layer called the **mantle**. With a depth of 2900 km, the mantle is considerably thicker than the crust.

The word 'mantle', like 'crust', refers to a form of covering. As the crust covers the mantle, the mantle wraps round the **core**. The core of the Earth is made of dense material, mostly iron and nickel. The distance from the core's surface to the centre of the Earth is estimated as 1400 km.

By comparison with these vast distances, human activity has scarcely scratched the Earth's surface: very deep mines go down only 3.5 km (just over 2 miles), and even an experimental borehole in Texas has been drilled to only 19 km (about 12 miles). Journeys to the centre of the Earth and out through the other side will constitute rather more of a problem than going round it in 80 days!

Rocks and minerals

The Earth's crust is made of rock. In some places, such as cliffs and mountains, the rock is exposed; but in many places it is hidden by water or by soil and the plants that grow in it.

We tend to think of rocks as large single chunks of material. Yet the loose sand on a beach is just as much rock to the scientist as the sandstone cliff from which it may have come. Although in everyday speech stones and pebbles are distinguished from rocks because of their size or shape, stones and pebbles are rock. Rocks do not need to be large, made of one single piece, or even hard. It is the nature of the material that counts: that is, rock is a particular type of material.

Rock is made of minerals, such as feldspar, mica and quartz. Minerals are naturally occurring solids which have the same chemical composition throughout. A rock may be made up of a single mineral or of a number of different minerals.

The picture on the left shows a common rock, granite; the three constituent minerals are recognizable as crystals of different colours. The exact kinds of mineral, and their colours, vary from one kind of granite to another.

The structure of granite

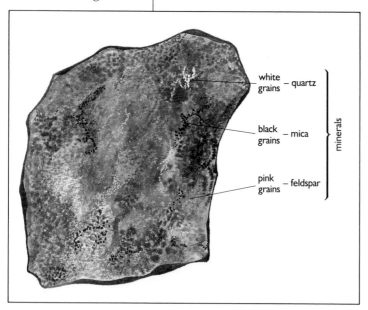

white grains — quartz

black grains — mica

pink grains — feldspar

minerals

The formation of rocks

There are three principal ways in which rocks have been formed.

The first is by the cooling of molten material which becomes solid. Rocks formed in this way are call *igneous*, after the Latin word *ignis*, fire. Examples include granite and basalt. Such rocks are still being formed by volcanoes, which bring liquid material from inside the Earth to the surface.

The second method of rock formation often starts with the breaking up of other rocks into small pieces through the action of water, wind and frost; and through chemical attack by substances in air and water. These small pieces are carried away by rivers or the sea, or as windblown sand. They finally arrive in the sea, where they sink and form a sediment. As layers of sediment build up, they compact the sediment underneath until it is compressed into a **sedimentary** rock. Sandstone is a rock that has sometimes been formed in this way, though much sandstone has also been formed in dry conditions in sand deserts (in some sand quarries in southern England you can see traces of sand dunes on the excavated face). Other kinds of sedimentary rock are formed when water dries up, depositing the minerals that were dissolved in it: for example, deposits of rock salt come from the evaporation of shallow seas. Yet another group of sedimentary rocks is made under the sea by the gradual accumulation of animal skeletons such as shells and corals; examples are limestone and chalk.

A metamorphosis is a change of form; such a process gives rise to the third type of rock. **Metamorphic** rocks are those whose crystal structure has been changed as a result of the intense heat and pressure deep in the Earth's crust. Shale, for example, is turned into slate, and limestone into marble by such a process.

Periods of rock formation in any one place are often followed by inactive periods. The effect of this is for rock to be put down in layers; these are known as **strata**.

Identifying minerals

Minerals can be studied and identified by using special microscopes, by chemical analysis and by examination of their physical properties. Of these, physical properties are the simplest and most direct way of identifying minerals. Appearance, while often informative, can be misleading.

Hardness is possibly the most revealing property. The hardness of a mineral is tested by scratching it with a standard mineral whose hardness is known. This may be one of ten minerals on a standard scale of hardness known as **Mohs' scale**. The softest mineral is numbered 1, the hardest 10.

1	talc (as in talcum powder)
2	gypsum (such as plaster of Paris)
3	calcite (such as limestone)
4	fluorite (also called fluorspar)
5	apatite (also found in tooth enamel)
6	orthoclase (a type of feldspar)
7	quartz (such as rock crystal)
8	topaz
9	corundum (such as ruby)
10	diamond

A mineral will show scratches from all things harder than itself, allowing it to be positioned on the scale. Alternatives to the standard minerals can be used: a fingernail, for example, is about 2.5 and a typical penknife blade 6.5.

The uses of rocks and minerals

Rock is familiar as a material for construction. Limestone, sandstone, marble and granite are all used as building stone; slate is cut for roofing and granite for kerbs; old fashioned natural paving stones in Britain are usually York sandstone. Though use in these ways has declined in recent years in Britain, large quantities of rock are still quarried for building roads and sea walls. Other building materials are manufactured from rock as a raw material: for example, cement is made from clay and limestone, and mixed with sand to make mortar, or sand and gravel to make concrete.

Minerals are the source of metals and other materials. Iron ore (which includes the mineral haematite) is processed to make iron. Glass is made mostly from sand. Gemstones are pieces of rare and beautiful minerals, which are cut and polished to show off their appearance to its best advantage.

Soil

Soil is generally thought of, by children and adults alike, as the material in which plants grow, providing both support and nutrients. This definition is adequate in some respects but it does not go far enough, as it refers only to the layer of soil that is normally seen. To obtain a fuller picture you have to dig down to the upper part of the rock that lies underneath. The cross-section thus exposed is called a soil profile. The profile reveals distinct layers which may be seen as three main divisions: parent material, subsoil and topsoil.

Soil profile

84

The **parent material** is the material from which the soil has developed, though this soil has often been carried away from directly above its parent material (see below). It is also called **bedrock**. This rock is more or less solid, but parts of it become broken off at its surface or along cracks, and begin to break down into soil.

Above the parent material these pieces get smaller, and this broken rock material forms the **subsoil**. Some of the soil particles may stick together, forming larger clumps of material. Roots may penetrate the subsoil, and there may be a small amount of plant and animal material. These small beginnings of living processes are the start of turning subsoil into topsoil.

Topsoil contains the decomposed remains of plants (humus) mixed with finely divided rock material. Topsoil is thus a mixture of materials from living and non-living sources.

There are spaces between the bits in the soil, filled with air and water. Soil is also a habitat for a variety of living things, such as worms.

The formation of soil

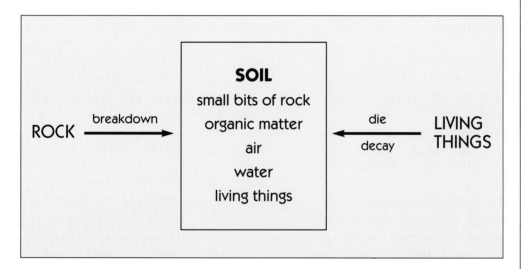

The formation of soil

The process of breaking down rock into the smaller bits which form part of soil is called **weathering**. Weathering is the name of a general process which in some cases is not caused by actual weather, as is described below.

Water plays a key role in weathering and the development of soil. It soaks down through any upper layers and into any cracks in the rock, or into the rock itself if this is porous. If this water then freezes it expands as it turns to ice, which may crack the rock. Even where freezing temperatures never occur, the difference between day and night temperatures causes the surface of the rock to expand and contract, so that eventually it cracks. Another kind of mechanical breakdown is caused by the ice of glaciers. Debris at the bottom of the moving ice scrapes across the underlying rock and scours it away. Water can also cause the chemical weathering of certain rocks: carbon dioxide from the air dissolves in water to form an acidic solution, which eats into the rock.

A second way in which water aids the development of soil is through its support of life. Living things such as plants can cause biological weathering of rocks; for instance, roots can grow into cracks in the rock and widen them. When living things die and decay, their remains mix with the particles of rock. Some organisms, such as earthworms and bacteria, help in the breakdown of this organic material.

The third role of water is in the way it reorganizes the soil particles by carrying material with it as it moves down through the soil.

Soils are formed above parent material, but this does not mean that any given soil is necessarily derived from the bedrock found beneath it. Soil can be transported by water, ice or wind, and laid down elsewhere. In Britain, for example, ice sheets have carried away much of the original soil cover from many parts of the country and laid it down many kilometres away. When the ice melted, the bare rock that had been stripped of its soil cover began to weather, forming new soil. In consequence, most soils in Britain have formed since the end of the last Ice Age, 10,000 years ago.

Differences in soils

Clearly the nature of the parent material affects the kind of soil formed. The sandy soil of the Lancashire coast is quite different in appearance from the chalky soil above the cliffs of Dover.

Soils differ in how they feel as well as how they look. The texture of a soil is due mainly to the size of the particles in it. Three categories of size are usually recognized: the largest is **sand** (from 2 mm down to 0.06 mm diameter); below this comes silt; and the smallest particles (less than 0.002 mm diameter) form clay. The feel of the soil depends on the proportions of sand, clay and silt: sandy soils feel gritty, while clay soils feel silky (or sticky when wet).

Another difference between soils is their structure; that is, the degree to which sand, clay or silt particles stick together. The water content of soils also varies from well drained through to waterlogged. The reason for these differences does not lie solely in the parent material. Climate also plays a role, especially rainfall. So does the shape of the land, with soil being washed downwards to accumulate at the foot of a slope. The degree of plant growth will affect the organic content of the soil. Finally, soils change over time, so that a younger soil differs from an older one based on the same parent material.

The diagram at the top of the next page portrays the relationship between rocks and soil, indicating how they are formed.

Landforms and landscape

The landforms we see today may look as if they have been there for ever. They have, however, been formed over millions of years by processes which are still continuing. Just as the landscape in Britain looked different thousands of years ago, so it will look different again in the future. We are used to much shorter time scales and so we barely notice the changes.

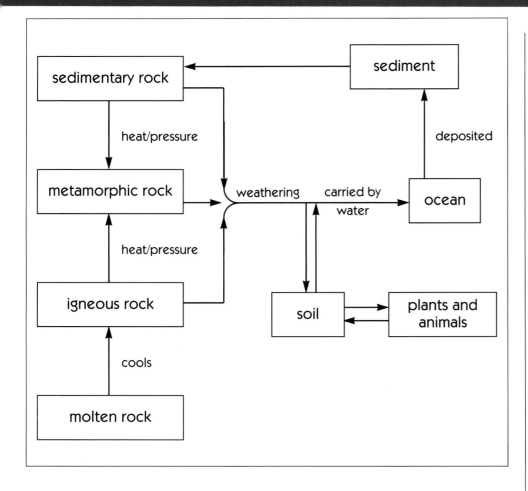

How rocks and soil are formed

The disintegration of rock through weathering is followed by the wearing away and transport of the debris; the whole process is known as **erosion**. Rivers, glaciers, waves and wind can all demolish and remove rock. They sculpt the scenery: rivers and glaciers carve out valleys while wind creates the peculiar shapes seen in the hills of some arid areas. Since eroded material mostly moves downwards under the influence of gravity, the overall effect of this process is to lower the land surface.

Different rock types are, however, eroded differently. While less resistant rocks are worn away to give low-lying land, more resistant rocks are left as uplands. At the coast, less resistant rocks (such as clay and chalk) are eroded to form bays, leaving headlands of more resistant rocks (such as limestone and granite).

The laying down of sediments has the effect of building up the land surface. Sedimentation is the putting down of the small bits of rock which have been carried by the agents of erosion. It occurs in the sea and estuaries, and on land as well. The windblown sands of deserts are sediments. The pressing together of sediments can lead to the formation of sedimentary rock (see 'The formation of rocks', above).

Since sediments are laid down in more or less horizontal layers, the combined effect of erosion and sedimentation is to flatten the Earth's surface to a featureless landscape. Much igneous rock is also laid down horizontally in the first instance. However, horizontal rock formations may be deformed by Earth movements. The Earth's crust consists of separate **plates**, huge chunks of crust and underlying mantle up to several thousand kilometres across, which are in constant slow movement, typically 2 to 5 cm a year (see below). As the plates move together the rock formations buckle and fold, rather like a carpet that rucks up on a slippery floor. The lifting up of the rock results in the formation of mountains. The Alps are an example of fold mountains that are relatively young.

More sudden changes to the landscape may take place during volcanic activity and earthquakes. Some eruptions under the seas have led to the creation of volcanic islands (for example the Hawaiian islands), while eruptions on some existing islands have blown them up, so that they disappear below sea level (for example Krakatau, destroyed in 1883). Only a small number (typically around 25) of the 500 or so active volcanoes in the world are in eruption at any one time. A few are in continuous eruption while the majority have dormant periods between relatively short times of activity.

Both liquid rock **(lava)** and gas come out of volcanoes. The mixture of these two under the Earth's surface is called **magma**. This is formed in the lower part of the Earth's crust and the upper few hundred kilometres of the mantle. Once released on to the surface of the Earth, the gas escapes and the lava solidifies as igneous rock.

The focus and epicentre of an earthquake

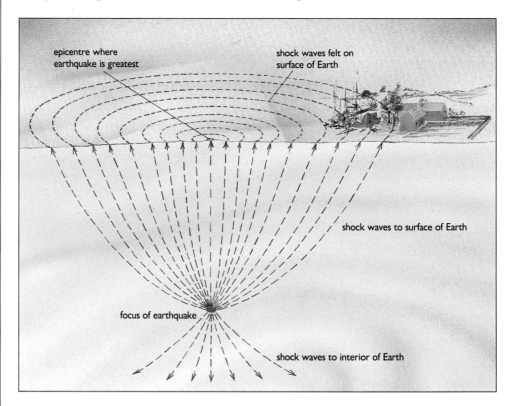

Most earthquakes occur where parts of the Earth are moving past each other along a plate boundary or a smaller crack – these discontinuities are called **faults**. The immense moving sections of rock may get stuck, building up stress and pressure. Sudden release of the stress causes vibrations which are transmitted through the rock. The point where unsticking occurs is known as the **focus** of the quake. The point on the Earth's surface vertically above the focus is the **epicentre**. The quaking of the ground may be sufficient to cause the surface to crack. These are not the only fearful consequences of the Earth's vibration: landslides may follow, and undersea quakes can cause enormous **tsunami** (commonly called 'tidal waves') which devastate the coast.

The Earth's movement is measured by a **seismometer**, which enables earthquakes to be assigned a number on the Richter scale. The scale takes account only of the size of the vibrations; it gives no indication of the duration of shaking.

In 1990 an earthquake in England registered about 5 on the scale. This might sound perilously close to the destructive San Francisco quake of 7.3 in the same year. However, an increase of one unit of the scale represents a tenfold increase in the size of the vibrations and a nearly hundredfold increase in energy. The severest earthquake measured happened in Assam, India, in 1897, measuring 8.7. The Alaska earthquake of 1964 rated 8.6.

When the positions of active volcanoes and the points of occurrence of sizeable earthquakes are examined a clear pattern emerges. They generally lie within narrow bands along interconnecting lines on the Earth's surface. These lines form the boundaries of the Earth's plates. There are at least 15 of these plates. Seven are particularly large, one underlying almost the whole of the Pacific Ocean, for example. The movement of these plates is generally thought to cause volcanic, earthquake and mountain-building activity alike, all of which occur at or near plate boundaries.

The shape of the plates has also influenced the form of some of the continents. The obvious fit between the outlines of the east coast of South America and the west coast of Africa reveals that they were once joined. About 100 million years ago, in the time of the dinosaurs, they began to drift apart, and are still moving.

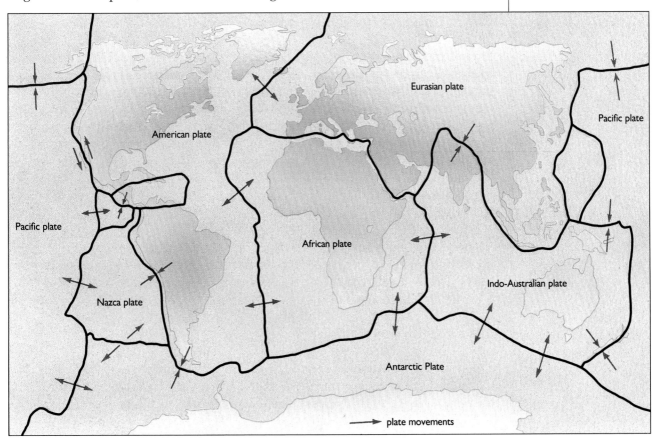

plate movements

Weather

The Earth's atmosphere

Four and a half billion years ago, as the newly formed Earth began to solidify, huge quantities of gas belched out from the surface. Even after the crust had formed, volcanoes kept on adding gas to the atmosphere. Initially it consisted mostly of carbon dioxide and nitrogen, with other gases such as methane, as well as water vapour – it was still too hot for liquid water to exist. Free oxygen came later, at first perhaps because of radiation from the Sun which split water molecules, but later and more importantly when the first plants extracted it from carbon dioxide.

The Earth is enveloped by air, held to the Earth by the force of gravity. Each square metre of the Earth's surface has about 10,000 kg of air above it (equivalent to 120 or so people). The pressure of the air, which varies around 100 kN/m² at sea level, can be measured with a **barometer**.

The air is not evenly distributed with height. As you go upwards, it thins out and so air pressure falls. There is no definite outer limit to the atmosphere, but it is regarded as being some hundreds of kilometres thick. Owing to the thinning out with height, about half the atmosphere lies below a height of 5 kilometres.

Temperature also changes with height, but in a more complex way than pressure. Four temperature layers can be distinguished. Our weather is largely determined by the behaviour of the atmosphere in the lowest of these layers, the **troposphere**. In this layer, temperature falls as height increases. The illustration at the top of the next page shows the structure of the atmosphere. The boundaries between layers occur at heights that vary from place to place above the Earth's surface. Heights shown are average values.

Part of the **stratosphere** contains ozone, a gas which is constantly formed from oxygen by ultraviolet radiation coming from the Sun. This **ozone layer** absorbs much of the ultraviolet radiation, preventing it from reaching the Earth's surface. Ozone is unstable and breaks up naturally, but it is broken up faster by chemical reactions precipitated by certain man-made gases – such as the notorious CFCs used in aerosol sprays and refrigerators, for cleaning and for making plastic foam. As the amount of ozone in the layer decreases, more ultraviolet radiation can penetrate, with harmful effects to animals and plants.

Air is a mixture of gases. The main two gases of the air that surrounds us are nitrogen and oxygen. In rough terms, moisture-free air is a mixture of four-fifths nitrogen and one-fifth oxygen. There are small percentages of other gases; the largest of these is argon at just under 1 per cent. The composition of the atmosphere remains largely the same up to 80 km above the Earth's surface. Above this, the oxygen and nitrogen gradually diminish as lighter gases take over.

There are also gases whose contribution to the mixture can be more variable. One of these, carbon dioxide, has a significant effect on the climate, even though it forms a relatively small percentage of the air (about 0.03 per cent). It allows sunlight through to warm the Earth's surface, but when the warm surface gives off infra-red radiation, the carbon dioxide absorbs this and will not let it escape into space. Because the glass in a greenhouse does the same thing, this is known as the **greenhouse effect**. The massive use of carbon based fuels such as coal and oil in recent years has led to a significant increase in carbon dioxide. The resultant warming of the atmosphere could melt part of the polar ice caps, which would raise sea level and flood low-lying countries such as Bangladesh. Carbon dioxide is not the only 'greenhouse gas'; another is methane, which is also increasing because of oil and natural gas extraction (natural gas is almost pure methane). Water vapour in the air also absorbs infra-red radiation. Note that the greenhouse effect is actually necessary to keep the Earth warm enough to live on; it is only when the effect is artificially stepped up that trouble begins.

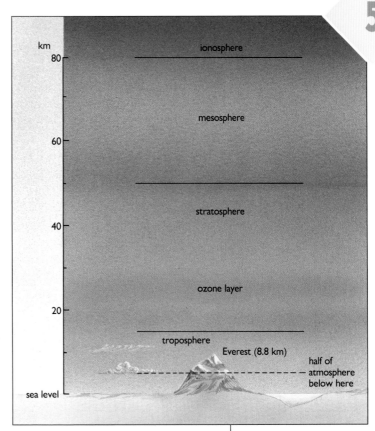

The Earth's atmosphere

The Sun and the weather

The fundamental cause of all weather on Earth is the Sun. This provides the energy which heats the atmosphere. Much of this heating takes place indirectly; that is, energy from the Sun warms the Earth itself and the Earth in turn radiates heat into its atmosphere. A lot of this re-radiated heat is absorbed in the atmosphere, especially by the 'greenhouse gases' (see the previous section). In contrast, on the Moon, where there is no atmosphere to retain heat, the temperature falls as low as −140 °C on the side away from the Sun.

The Earth's surface does not receive the Sun's heat and light evenly. The diagram on the right shows why polar regions are colder than equatorial ones. (The seasonal variation of these effects is described in the *Earth in Space* teachers' guide.)

The effects of latitude on the heating of the Earth

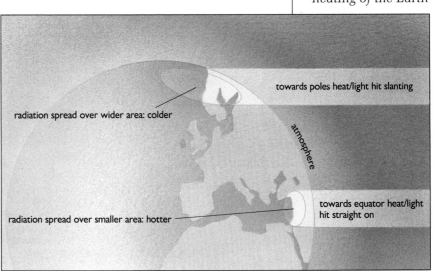

Winds

There is another consequence of this unequal distribution of the Sun's heat. When air is heated it expands, becoming less dense and lighter than cold air, and with a lower pressure. Therefore there is a region of relatively low pressure around the Equator. Air moves into this region from the north and south to equalize the pressure difference. The warm equatorial air, being lighter than this incoming cool air, rises above it and spreads out. As it does so it cools and descends again. So there is a constant circulation of air between the Equator and the Poles. This is wind.

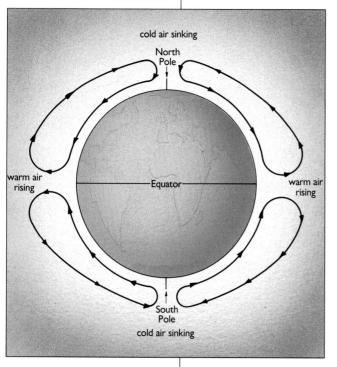

The flow of air on Earth

The diagram on the left gives a highly simplified account of the world's air circulation. In the northern hemisphere, surface winds blow from the north. This southward flowing wind is called a northerly wind. Winds are named according to the direction they come from, since this reveals more about the weather they bring than where they blow to.

This north–south pattern of wind would exist only if the Earth stood still (and its surface were smooth). However, the Earth is spinning. The rotation of the Earth from west to east causes winds in the northern hemisphere to swerve to their right, as shown in the diagrams below. (You can model this by dropping a marble near the centre of a revolving record player turntable, though the effect is seen in reverse because the turntable is going clockwise.) The northerly winds become north-easterlies near the Equator, as can be seen from the world wind map in an atlas.

These are the prevailing winds in latitudes between the Equator and 30° N (North Africa). In the region from 30° N to 60° N where Britain is located, the northward flowing upper winds fall to become surface winds and swing to move towards a north-east direction. These are, therefore, south-west winds, but are usually called westerlies. The prevailing winds in Britain are westerlies bringing air from over the Atlantic.

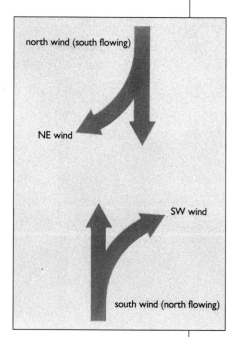

The effect of the Earth's rotation on the wind

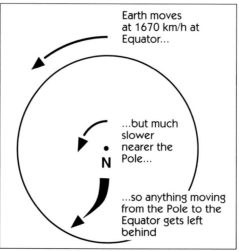

Moisture in the air

Water can be in the air in three forms:

◆ as an invisible gas, water vapour;
◆ as droplets of liquid in clouds, rain, mist and fog;
◆ as solid snow, hail or ice crystals in clouds.

Humidity is the term used to indicate how full of moisture (water vapour) air is. It can be used to predict rain. The toy from which a model figure emerges with an umbrella to predict rain works through a strand of gut absorbing moisture and twisting as the dampness of the air changes.

Air can hold more moisture when it is warm. If its temperature falls it is unable to hold so much moisture. The water vapour condenses as tiny drops of water. When this happens at ground level, dew forms. When it happens in mid air it gives mist, fog or clouds.

Clouds form when warm air rises; as temperature falls with increasing height, at a certain point water vapour condenses (just as the invisible hot steam cools and condenses as visible clouds of liquid water droplets coming out of a kettle). Droplets of liquid water and ice crystals float in the cloud. Two processes within the cloud lead to precipitation; that is, water in some form falling from the sky. Droplets of water merge together, and if they reach a certain size (about 0.5 mm) they fall. Water drops may also stick to ice particles in the cloud. Again, when these are sufficiently heavy, they fall. If they melt on the way down, it rains. If not, it hails. Snow is another solid form of precipitation, formed by ice crystals slowly building up inside the cloud to form flakes.

Clouds appear to move through the atmosphere. In reality, they move with it; that is, they are the visible part of a moving mass of air.

Weather forecasts and measurements

Weather forecasting is a form of scientific prediction. It is arrived at by accumulating information about present conditions over a wide area and interpreting this in the light of expected movements of air.

Among the factors measured which may provide information about future weather are:

◆ air temperature;
◆ air pressure, and whether it is rising or falling;
◆ wind direction and speed;
◆ cloud type and cover (how much cloud there is);
◆ humidity;
◆ visibility (how clear the air is).

National weather offices receive regular reports from weather stations on land and at sea. Some of these stations are automatic ones which transmit signals of the measurements taken by their instruments. Information is also collected from observations taken on board ships.

The measurements from each place are shown on a chart. This provides a synopsis of the weather at a particular time. Extremely powerful computers analyse a sequence of these summary charts and predictions are made of the likely look of the charts over the following few days. Simplified versions of the predicted charts appear as the weather maps we see in newspapers.

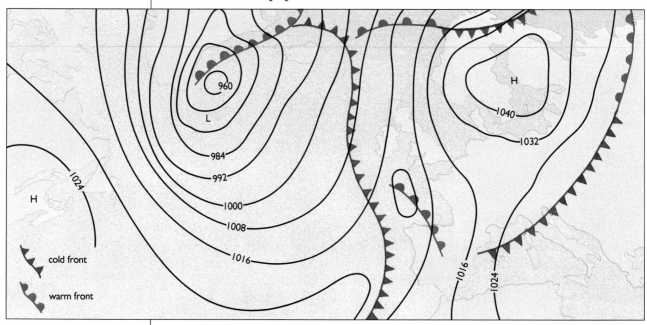

A particularly important feature of these maps is the isobars – lines joining together places where pressure is equal. They outline areas of low pressure – **depressions**, marked L on the map – and areas of high pressure – **anticyclones** – marked H. Winds in a depression revolve towards the centre to equalize the low pressure and so, in the northern hemisphere, in an anti-clockwise direction.

Depressions form when cold, polar air comes into contact with warm, tropical air. The boundaries between these air masses are known as fronts (the chart shows how these are represented). Fronts strongly influence the weather patterns in temperate climates such as that of Britain. In a warm front warm air follows cold, while in a cold front the opposite occurs. In a depression the warm front precedes the cold front. Both kinds of front bring rain, since at the boundary cold air cools the warm, moist air and condenses the water vapour. Depressions bring changeable and wet weather; there is a calmer, milder period between the two fronts.

Anticyclones move slowly and bring settled, dry weather. The sky is frequently clear, so that in summer when hours of sunshine are long and nights are short, the weather is warmer than average. In winter when the sun appears only for a short time, the net effect of the clear sky is to allow heat to escape, so the weather is frosty.

Weather predictions are also shown on maps. A number of conventional symbols are used to represent likely temperatures, wind speeds and directions, and cloud, sun or rain.

Weather stations produce information about the atmosphere at ground level. Measurements taken higher up add to the accuracy of forecasts. This information is gained from aircraft and from radiosondes, which are balloons to which a radio transmitter and instruments to measure pressure, temperature and humidity are attached. These rise as high as 20 km before bursting and parachuting to the ground.

Rainfall varies greatly from place to place, even between points quite close together, as it is affected by local variations in the height of the land. Radar is now often used to detect rainfall. The falling drops of rain reflect radio waves to give an image on the screen, allowing computers to build up a picture of the pattern of rain.

Another refinement in weather forecasting has been the use of satellites. The pictures they provide are particularly useful because they cover large areas of the Earth. They reveal cloud patterns, including the position of depressions, which may be recognized by the spiral shape of the clouds swirling towards the centre.

Long-range forecasts are based on a different system. They rely mainly on matching present patterns to similar conditions in the same month of previous years. The forecast is then based on what actually happened in those previous years. Forecasting events even a month ahead is, however, a chancy business, as there are so many factors involved and if even one of them deviates from what is expected, it affects everything else.

air (topic) 13-14, 61
    composition 90-91
    movement *see* wind
    pressure 90
    in soil 52
anticyclones 94
assessment 11, 74-80
atmosphere 27, 61, 90-1
Attainment Target 1 74-76

barometer 90
basalt 83
bedrock 84
building stone 55, 84

carbon dioxide 90-1
cement 84
CFCs 90
chalk 83
Channel Tunnel 47
classifying 8, 77
clay 86
clouds 13, 61, 93
    children's ideas 65-6
    records 70-1
    satellite patterns 95
compost heap 50
concrete 84
core (Earth) 48, 82
cross-curricular topics 12-14, 15-16

depressions 94
digging holes 46

Earth
    crust 27, 28, 48, 81, 82
    models 47, 48
    origins 81
    rotation 92
        children's ideas 65
    structure 8, 44, 48, 81-2
        children's ideas 35-7
Earth in Space 91
earthquakes 27, 28, 29, 59, 87-89
    children's ideas 34, 42, 43
    shock waves 81-2
epicentre (earthquake) 88
erosion 59, 87
    children's ideas 42, 79
Experimental and Investigative
    Science 10-11

farms and farming (topic) 12-13, 54
faults 88
focus (of earthquake) 88
folklore 67, 72
fronts (weather) 94

gemstones 84
glass 84
granite 82, 83, 84
greenhouse effect 91

hardness
    minerals 83
    rocks 40, 41, 56, 75
holes in ground 46-7
humidity 93
humus 84
    children's ideas 30

ice, effect on rocks 85-6
igneous rocks 27, 28, 83, 86
information technology 14, 51
iron ore 84
isobars 94

landforms 29, 58-59, 87-89
    children's ideas 33-4, 41-3
landscape 8, 12, 87-89
    children's ideas 33-4, 43
    rocks and 55-59
lava 87-88
limestone 83, 84
Living processes 32
living things in soil 52-3, 85
Living things in their environment 29

magma 87-88
man-made 'stone' 55
mantle (Earth) 48, 82
marble 83, 84
Materials 29, 55
metamorphic rocks 27, 28, 83
methane 91
minerals 56, 82
    identification 83
    uses 84
Mohs' scale of hardness 83
Moon, temperatures 91
mortar 84
Mount Pinatubo 59
mountain formation 29, 59, 87, 89
    children's ideas 42

Napoleon (retreat from Moscow) 72

ozone 13, 90

parent material (soil) 84
planning science programme 22-24
plant growth in soil 32, 53-4
plaster of Paris, 'weathering' 58
plates (Earth's crust) 27, 28, 29, 87, 89
pupils' books 14, 17-21

radar 95
radiosondes 95
rainfall 93, 95
    measurement 61, 71
resources 25
Richter scale 88
rift valleys 29
rock salt 83
rocks 8, 29, 82
    children's ideas 32-3, 39-40
        assessment 75-79
    chipping, safety considerations 25
    formation 40, 83, 86
    hardness 40, 41, 56, 75
    and landscape 55-59
    in soil 50
    types 27, 28, 50-1
    underground 8, 29, 39, 47
    uses 84
    see also weathering
rocks and soils (theme) 8, 27, 28-59
Rocks, soil and weather and *More about rocks, soil and weather* 14, 17-21, 49, 52, 54, 55, 56, 57, 59, 71, 72, 73

safety 25-26
sand 86
sandstone 83, 84
    absorbency 75-6
satellites 8, 66, 95
Scottish guidelines 9
seasonal changes 8, 27, 60
sedimentary rocks 27, 28, 83, 87
sediments 83, 87
seismometer 88
silt 86
slate 83, 84
soil profiles 46, 47, 51

soils 8, 12, 13, 29, 84, 84-5
    air in 52
    characteristics 27, 28
    children's ideas 31-2, 37-39
        assessment 75-79
    composition 27, 28, 48-49
    living things in 52-3
    origins 49-50, 79, 85-6
    plant growth in 32, 53-4
    safety considerations in work with
        25-26
    survey 54-5
    types 29, 32, 50-1, 86
    water in 51-2
    see also erosion
sorting materials 8, 56
SPACE approach 5, 7
Spanish Armada 72
stone trail 55
strata 83
stratosphere 90
subsoil 84
    children's ideas 30
Sun
    avoiding looking at 25
    effect on weather 27, 60, 91, 92
sunshine records 70
sweetcorn 54

temperature 61
    measurement 70
thermometers 25
'tidal waves' 88
time scale 59
topsoil 84
transport (soil and sediments) 58, 85-86
troposphere 90
tsunami 88

underground structure 8, 29, 44, 46-48
    children's ideas 30, 35-7

Variety of life 59
volcanoes 27, 28, 29, 59, 83, 87-89
    children's ideas 34, 43

water (topic) 13, 14, 15-16
    absorption by rocks 75-6
    in atmosphere 91, 93
    effects on rocks 29, 57-58, 85
    in soil 51-2
    transport by 58
water cycle 71
    children's ideas, assessment 80
weather (theme) 8, 27, 60-73, 90-93
    children's ideas 62-7
    effects 63, 72-3
weather forecasting 8, 61, 71, 93-5
    children's ideas 62-3, 65, 66-7
weather maps 94-5
weather stations 93, 95
    children's 68, 70-1
weathering 8, 27, 28, 57-8, 59, 85-6
    children's ideas 33, 41-3
        assessment 78-79
winds 61, 67, 92
    in depressions 94
    effects 72
    records 70
    transport by 58
worms 52-3, 85
    children's ideas 39